HALF-WAY TO THE MOON

Half-way to the Moon

New Writing From Russia

Edited by

PATRICIA BLAKE and
MAX HAYWARD

HOLT, RINEHART AND WINSTON
New York   Chicago   San Francisco

First published in the United States September 1964

Library of Congress Catalog Card Number: 64-19872

First Edition
80981-0114

Printed in Great Britain

Copy 2

PG
3213
B56
Cop. 2
Under Grad.
Collection

CONTENTS

Contents

INTRODUCTION

Et l'art réunit . . .
là où la tyrannie sépare

ALBERT CAMUS

'PASTERNAK WAS my only master,' said the young Russian poet, Andrei Voznesensky, when I met him in Moscow in August of 1962. In 1954, when Voznesensky was twenty-one, he received a letter from Pasternak praising his first poems and inviting him to come and see him.

'From that time on I never left his side,' Voznesensky said. 'I moved out to Peredelkino and stayed near him until his death. When he died I felt that someone had come out of myself—out of my being. I felt utterly alone. I wanted to die. Then, I thought, someone must continue Pasternak's work. And now I'm no longer alone . . .'

It is true that Voznesensky is no longer alone. The most important change that has taken place on the Russian literary scene since Stalin is that the poets, the prose writers, and the playwrights—together with their public—have gradually ceased to suffer from the old, fearful sense of isolation. This development, in one decade, seems very nearly miraculous when one considers how effectively Stalin's attempt to atomize Soviet society interrupted intellectual and human discourse. The reflex of distrust, the habit of hypocrisy among individuals were merely symptoms of a sickness hitherto considered fatal: man's alienation from his own truth. So pervasive and so damaging was the thirty-year terror that only heroes, lunatics, and possibly poets like Pasternak might impose either reason or imagination on the reality of the human condition under Stalin.

Yet a genuine literary intelligentsia has come into being

during this decade, composed not only of young writers whose experience with Stalinism had been slight, but also of some older authors, like Konstantin Paustovsky, who have endured the entire Stalin era. The spirit of mutual encouragement, and common cause which prevails among them is astonishing to any foreign visitor who has lately experienced the ferocious climate of literary life in, say, New York, Paris or London. Until recently, these writers were able to spend a good part of their time promoting their colleagues, battling for the publication of each other's work, manoeuvring to get their protégés into the Writers' Union, defending one another in the press against the conservative critics, and making arrangements to bring promising young people from the provinces where they might develop in a more congenial atmosphere. Conversation with these writers is quite unlike the ceremonious evasions and circumlocutions one had become accustomed to among Soviet intellectuals. Clearly this new intelligentsia has recovered that internal integrity which seemed shattered under Stalin and which is, of course, the precondition of literature.

Indeed, it appeared that after three decades of near-barrenness, Russia was again producing literature—burgeonings perhaps by her nineteenth-century standards, but nonetheless splendidly promising. This development began during the 'thaw' in 1956 among the writers clustered around the ill-fated almanac *Literary Moscow*, but was harshly arrested after the Hungarian Revolution by Khrushchev ('our hand will not tremble . . .' he threatened the writers) who was in no mood for anything remotely resembling a Petoefi Circle at home. There followed a period of brave failures, and evidently, literature 'for the drawer'. Then for roughly three years (until the cultural crackdown of 1963) scarcely a month passed when a young writer or poet did not publish a work of the imagination, each bolder in form and substance than the last. The purpose of this collection is to introduce some of this new writing to Western readers who, understandably, have become accustomed to regarding contemporary Russian literature in terms of the cant, the dreary didacticism, and the onward-and-upward themes of 'socialist realism'. The editors submit that the works in this book, each in its own way, have served to restore Russian literature to the modern conscience.

For a brief period, then, literature offered what no totalitarian system can long tolerate: a forum for individual expression. As such, the new writing has had a resonance which is inconceivable in the West. 'Every wall has a door,' said my neighbour at a Moscow poetry reading in September 1962, 'and these young people have found it.' What had happened was that the verse of such poets as Evtushenko, Voznesensky, Akhmadulina, and Vinokurov, the stories of Kazakov, Aksyonov and Nagibin, the novels and essays of Nekrasov, the plays of Volodin and Rozov, found an echo among a vast number of people who discovered at last that they too were not alone—that there existed others who could both articulate and share their yearnings, their preoccupations, their tastes. These people are by no means all students. Voznesensky told a *Times* correspondent that his readers are mainly members of the 'technological intelligentsia': 'There are millions of them in Russia now. Many of them work on sputniks and other enormously complicated machines and they want poetry to be complicated too. They have no use for rhymed editorials . . .'

It is the poets who communicate most directly to Soviet readers, possibly because of the traditional response to poetry in Russia, but more likely because the immediacy of the form meets the urgency of the need. 'Poetry,' wrote Mallarmé, 'is the language of a state of crisis.' Editions of 100,000 copies of Evtushenko's books have sold out within the first forty-eight hours of publication. Advance orders alone for Voznesensky's last book of verse, *The Triangular Pear* (1962), reached 100,000 two months before its publication. The poetry sections of Soviet book stores are fully stocked, however, with works by the old-guard poets which remain unsold from year to year. The quite inadequate size of printings of books by the new poets may have contributed to the rage for public readings which recently seized Russia—until both printings and readings were halted in the winter of 1963. The most spectacular of these readings took place in

November 1962 in Moscow's Luzhniki Sports Stadium where 14,000 people gathered to hear Voznesensky, Akhmadulina and Boris Slutsky. Poetry readings on a more modest scale had become the principal entertainment of intellectuals and students in Moscow, and in provincial towns as well, where poets went by the truckload. Even Mayakovsky, who spent his lifetime travelling across Russia declaiming his verse, never commanded anything like the following of these young people.[1]

The hopes of 1962 were perhaps best expressed by the poet Alexander Tvardovsky: 'In art and literature, as in love, one can lie only for a while; sooner or later comes the time to tell the truth.' In November of that year an event had taken place which suggested that the time might have arrived at last. This was the publication of Alexander Solzhenitsyn's devastating novel of conditions in a Stalinist prison camp, *One Day in the Life of Ivan Denisovich*, by order of Khrushchev himself and of the Central Committee. The writers' response was described in 1963 by Khrushchev: 'It is said that periodicals and publishing houses are being flooded with manuscripts about the life of people in deportation, prisons and camps. This is a very dangerous theme.' The response of the novel's hundreds of thousands of readers has not been officially noted but, judging from later developments, it seems clear that it raised in the minds of many that most 'dangerous' of themes: the responsibility of the present bureaucracy for Stalinism. Evidently Khrushchev has been late in learning the lesson of every Russian ruler since Nicholas I: the power of literature to arouse the conscience of a people and disclose the essence of tyranny.

---

[1] Unfortunately, modern music and painting have proved less accessible (in every sense) to the general public. As these new works have very rarely been performed or exhibited, public taste has not developed much beyond Rimsky-Korsakov and Repin. Impressionism is still considered, by both the authorities and the public, as the utmost limit of modernism. Moreover, because the Party has been least permissive in the interpretation of socialist realism in these arts, music and painting are recovering far more slowly from the dreary academicism imposed on them for so many years. The plight of the modern painter is particularly acute; always the chief butt of the philistines, he is their captive in the Soviet Union. As Yuri Kazakov's story in this book suggests, the painter is often a desolate figure; frustrated and demoralized, he feels remote from the (until now) more fortunate literary intelligentsia.

Russia's creative artists confronted the first phase of the purge in a mood of confidence and solidarity against the philistines. For since December 1, 1962, when Khrushchev visited the exhibition of non-representational art at Moscow's Manege Hall, the rallying cry of the philistines had again been heard across the land: 'Such pictures were not painted by the hand of man but by the tail of a donkey!' At the first of the meetings of the Ideological Commission of the Central Committee, held *in camera* in December with 400 artists, composers and writers, Evtushenko protested against the charge that Russia's foremost sculptor, Ernst Neizvestny, is guilty of producing unpatriotic 'formalist' art. Evtushenko is reported to have said: 'Neizvestny came back from the war his body criss-crossed with wounds; I hope he will live many more years and produce many more fine works of art.'

'As people say,' Khrushchev retorted, 'only the grave corrects a hunchback.'

Evtushenko's answer: 'I hope we have outlived the time when the grave is used as a means of correction.'

At the same meeting, Leonid Ilichev, the head of the Ideological Commission, read (for purposes of refutation) a letter of protest addressed to Khrushchev and signed by prominent figures in the arts:

Unless a variety of artistic trends can exist, art is doomed . . . We now see how artists who have followed a single trend—the only trend which flourished under Stalin and which did not permit others to work or even to live—are beginning to interpret what you said at the exhibition . . . We ask you to stop this return to past methods which are contrary to the whole spirit of our times.

Among the signers were the writers Simonov and Ehrenburg, the composer Shostakovich and the film director Romm—men who had little in common up to now but their compromises under Stalin. One of the signers of a second, similar letter was later revealed to be none other than Alexei Surkov, the former Secretary of the Writers' Union, long considered one of the most unreconstructed Stalinists of them all.

The extent of the Party's anxiety about the new intelligentsia was reflected in Ilichev's speeches of December 17 and 26, 1962:

> In certain discussions among intellectuals it is now con-
> sidered indecent and old-fashioned to defend the correct
> Party positions; to do so is to appear to be a reactionary,
> a conservative, to lay oneself open to the accusation of
> dogmatism, sectarianism, narrow-mindedness, backward-
> ness, Stalinism, etc. . . . It is one thing to combat the con-
> sequences of the cult of personality in order to assert the
> Leninist standards of life . . . and another to deal blows,
> under the guise of the struggle against these consequences,
> to our ideology, our life—in a word—to socialism and
> communism.

However ominous these declarations, they suggested a certain confusion within the Central Committee which was
certainly not present when Zhdanov bore down upon the arts
in 1946.[1] The intellectuals were given 'warning', but were
assured that there would be no more witch hunts. In fact,
the writers were invited to join the Party in rooting out the
'aftermath of the cult of personality in all spheres of life'.
Unfortunately, the aftermath of Ilichev's speeches consisted
in the restoration of some of the most notorious Stalinist

[1] The most sinister aspect of the December meetings were the denunciations
of Ehrenburg which portended Khrushchev's massive onslaught on him in
March. According to Michel Tatu of *Le Monde*, Serebryakova (the widow of
the Old Bolshevik) accused Ehrenburg not only of political crimes, but of
felonies 'so grave and so incredible that it would be unseemly to report
them here'. Incredible too is the witness she invoked against Ehrenburg:
Alexander Poskrebyshev, Stalin's personal secretary—who was long thought
dead, but who in fact is living and writing his memoirs!

At the same meeting, Tatu reported, Nikolai Gribachev, a candidate member of the Central Committee, did not hesitate to use the word 'cosmopoli-
tanism' in connexion with Ehrenburg's patronage of modern art. The old
guard writers and painters at once seized the opportunity thus offered them
to open fire on a man who, whatever his degree of compromise with Stalinism
in the past, has been one of the most eloquent and effective opponents of
the survivals of Stalinism. The author of the most scurrilous of these attacks
was the critic Vladimir Ermilov who has been expert at denunciations since
1930 when he accused Mayakovsky of being a tool of the Trotskyist opposition.
In *Izvestiya*, January 30, 1963, Ermilov attacked Ehrenburg for 'unethical'
behaviour during Stalin's purges; since Ehrenburg knew the facts (as he had
stated in his memoirs), unlike 'ordinary citizens' such as Ermilov, he should
have spoken out against them. The accusations of Serebryakova and Ermilov
were evidently to the liking of Khrushchev who, in his zeal to extricate himself from his own complicity with Stalinism, was himself soon to use Ehrenburg
as a scapegoat.

diehards to positions of influence in the arts. One by one Stalin's old cultural commissars, the hacks, the 'dogmatists' replaced the men of the 'thaw' on the editorial boards of publishing houses, newspapers and magazines, and in the leadership of the Moscow Writers' Union, the Academy of Arts, and the State cinema organization. Even eighty-two-year-old Alexander Gerasimov, Stalin's court painter for twenty years, reappeared briefly on the scene. Gerasimov, whose portraits of Stalin in every conceivable pose vanished some time ago from the nation's museums, at last found the time and place (*Trud*, January 9, 1963) to avenge himself on a whole series of persons and publications which he claimed had promoted 'formalist art'—including the journal *Ogonyok*, edited by the arch-conservative Sofronov, and *Nedelya*, edited by Azhubei, Khrushchev's son-in-law. Gerasimov remarked, 'One must call things by their name, cite names and facts,' thereby demonstrating to every honest man in Russia the hopelessness of doing just that.

In the midst of this confusion, Evtushenko left for a tour of West Germany and France apparently still confident of the ultimate victory of the liberals over the 'dogmatists'. In the French weekly *L'Express* he published a 'precocious autobiography' in which he made some compelling observations regarding the cynicism, the mendacity, the self-interest, and the anti-semitism of the dogmatists who, he wrote, have betrayed not only the Revolution but Russia herself. Other remarks suggested more recklessness than confidence: 'In Russia all tyrants have believed poets to be their worst enemies.' Most reckless of all was perhaps his statement at a press conference in Paris on February 12: ' . . . When one speaks of that period (the Stalin era), I think not only of Stalin. I think too of his accomplices, of those who helped him, sometimes urged him on, and of those who were silent.' On March 4, Evtushenko was summarily called home to Moscow to face the dogmatists, who were waiting for him, teeth bared—and Nikita Khrushchev himself.

On March 8 Khrushchev delivered himself of a 15,000-word

speech in which, among other things, he confided to the
nation his personal tastes in all the arts. However compelling
these preferences,[1] the political motives revealed in his
speech loom much larger as an explanation for the purge.
Behind the great tangle of Khrushchev's verbiage, the outline
of his main concerns is plainly perceptible. The first is, of
course, the erosion of ideology and Party controls in the arts
per se. Henceforth, he said, anyone who maintains that formalism and abstractionism can 'peacefully co-exist' with
socialist realism will be regarded as an anti-communist.
The second is the alienation of young people from their
elders, whom they often consider contaminated, if not
utterly compromised by Stalinism. The authority of the
Party is threatened when Soviet youth is seen to respond
with more enthusiasm to the young poetry than to agit-prop.
Khrushchev's repeated denial of any estrangement between
'fathers and sons' is a measure of his alarm. He denounced,
for example, the thirty-one-year-old poet Robert Rozhdestvensky for allegedly having said that the 'sentiments of our
youth are expressed solely by a group of young authors and
that these authors are the tutors of our youth'. 'That is
certainly not so,' said Khrushchev. 'Our youth has been
brought up by the Party, it follows the Party and sees in it its
teacher and leader.'

Khrushchev's third, and evidently most important concern
is the matter which was raised by Ilya Ehrenburg in a chapter of his memoirs. By writing that he was aware at the time
that innocent people were arrested under Stalin, Ehrenburg,
by inference, (and perhaps by inadvertence) suggested that
others, in far higher places, must have been equally aware.
This suggestion is, of course, intolerable to Khrushchev whose
claim to authority rests on his alleged ignorance at the time
of the crimes of his late colleague. To prove his point, Khrushchev was moved to tell of the tears he shed at Stalin's bier,
and to describe the Stalin era as 'bright, happy years, years

[1] In music, Khrushchev is enraptured by the *Internationale* and the songs
of General Budyonny's cavalry. In sculpture, by a monument to Karl Marx.
In poetry, by an agit-prop jingle of Civil War days entitled *How my Mother
Saw me off to the War*. In sum, art is an 'ideological weapon' whose function
is to 'crush our enemies' and 'summon people to military accomplishments
and work'.

of struggle and victories, of the triumph of communist ideas.'

The Stalinist hacks Khrushchev had unleashed now proceeded to vent their pent-up anger and jealousy on nearly every young writer who had received public acclaim during the last years—particularly Evtushenko and Voznesensky. In the press, and at writers' meetings all over the country, they proclaimed an end to the editions of 100,000 copies, the favourable reviews, and the trips abroad for writers who flout Party opinion, play the game of Western *bourgeois* ideologists ('with one foot on Gorky Street and the other on Broadway') in their 'rotten, overpraised, unrealistic, smelly writings'. In classic purge style, recantations were demanded. Here, however, the results obtained were far from satisfactory. Many maintained silence. Others apparently defended themselves; although the liberals were scarcely offered a forum by the Soviet press, reports from foreign communist observers indicated widespread defiance at the writers' meetings. Even excerpts of confessions fit to print in *Literary Gazette* were often, like Voznesensky's and Rozhdestvensky's, ambiguous or ironic. Only Evtushenko, and Aksyonov, plainly under formidable pressure,[1] yielded something like recantations.

The principal figure in the writers' resistance was, however, no foolhardy youngster, untouched by memories of Stalinism, but the fifty-one-year-old Victor Nekrasov—war-hero, Party member, and Stalin prize novelist. His travel essays *On Both Sides of the Ocean* (see p. 222) had provoked Khrushchev into one of his most ferocious outbursts; on March 8 he had accused Nekrasov of 'proclaiming a principle utterly unacceptable for our art'. Khrushchev objected particularly to Nekrasov's praise of the directors of the film *Ilyich's Gate* for 'not dragging in the old worker with greying moustaches who understands all and has a clear answer for everything. If he had come along with his instructive phrases, it would have killed the picture.' Said Khrushchev: 'And this is written by a Soviet writer in a Soviet magazine!

[1] How formidable may be gauged by the following report in *Literary Gazette*: 'Evtushenko attempted to dispute the sharp criticism directed at him . . . but under the influence of the exacting, principled atmosphere of the Plenary Session (of the Writers' Union) Evtushenko was nevertheless forced to talk of his mistakes.'

One cannot read without indignation such things written in a lordly, scornful tone about an old worker. I think the tone of such talk is absolutely impermissible for a Soviet writer.'

However 'impermissible' Nekrasov's writings, it became clear during the weeks that followed that their author could not be made to recant. In April, at a meeting of intellectuals in Kiev, Nikolai Podgorny (then First Secretary of the Ukrainian Party) complained that Nekrasov had denied any wrongdoing and had said that he would write only 'the truth, the great truth, the genuine truth'. Nekrasov, Podgorny added, 'has learned nothing and, indeed, has no desire to do so. As all of you heard, he considers an admission of guilt to be demeaning to him as a communist. For what truth do you stand, Comrade Nekrasov? Your speech and the ideas you continue to maintain have a strong flavour of petty-*bourgeois* anarchy. The Party, the people, cannot and will not tolerate this.'

The next step was to disperse the writers; it was announced that Voznesensky was spending his time in factories in the Vladimir region, that Aksyonov was going to a construction site in Siberia, and that Rozhdestvensky had 'already plunged into the masses'. Simultaneously, 170 little-known but certifiably 'genuine Soviet writers' were rounded up in the provinces for a Moscow conference of young writers, in a clumsy and (judging from the samples of their work in the press) hopeless attempt to offer the reading public new heroes for old. Khrushchev's exasperation was reflected in his speech of June 21 at the Central Committee Plenum on ideology; he denounced those who were persisting in their incorrect views, singling out Nekrasov for not having 'recognized the demands of the Party' and, therefore, 'opposing the Party line'.

He called for Nekrasov's expulsion from the Party and to illustrate how far he might go in dealing with recalcitrants, he drew an example from Gogol: 'Taras Bulba killed his own son, Andrei, for going over to the side of the enemy. Such is the logic of the struggle.'

The threats and the abuse heaped on the liberal intelligentsia for seven months were, of course, dreadfully familiar—a reminder, if one was needed, that the apparatus of oppression remains intact and can be turned on full force at any moment. And indeed, by the end of June, it seemed that nothing short of violence could put down the intellectuals' resistance. The price of using overt Stalinist methods was, however, too high for Khrushchev; such a decision would compromise the entire political and economic programme he has advanced since 1956 on the ideological grounds of 'de-Stalinization'. Moreover, the intensification of the dispute with China now required an appearance of national unity and foreign Party solidarity[1] against the enemy. Thus, the cultural offensive lost its momentum. As no action was forthcoming against the writers (Nekrasov was not even expelled from the Party), threats and denunciations were by now utterly unavailing. The authorities had to settle—for the time being at any rate—for an undeclared truce with the liberals who could now, at least, be expected to understand the limits of their actions in the present and of their expectations in the future.

There followed some signs of appeasement of liberal opinion such as the appearance of a few poems (on 'acceptable' themes: Lenin and Cuba) by Voznesensky and Evtushenko. More surprising has been the staying-power of the fifty-three-year-old poet, Alexander Tvardovsky—the only liberal to have preserved a position of influence on the cultural scene, despite the fact that his journal, *Novy mir*, had published the very works (Ehrenburg and Nekrasov) Khrushchev had found most offensive. On August 18 1963, the most improbable publication of the Soviet 60's appeared in *Izvestiya*: Tvardovsky's long fable in verse, *Tyorkin in the Other World*.

Purportedly yet another 'acceptable' satire on the Stalin era, the poem takes a simple Russian soldier, who has been killed in the Second World War, on a journey through the communist purgatory: a Stalinist 'other world' which is scarcely distinguishable from the here and now. The soldier finds a Bureau meeting 'with the majesty of real life':

---

[1] In this context, the protests of some Soviet bloc and Western Communist parties—notably the Italian Party—against the cultural offensive in Russia no doubt contributed to its abatement. It is interesting to note that among the first, tentative reappearances in print of the condemned writers were veiled attacks on the Chinese by Ehrenburg, Evtushenko and Voznesensky.

Evidently taking up the case
Of an individual at fault—what pleasure . . .
A deceased one was confessing errors
(And, of course, he lied.)

The bourgeois hell (visible through a peephole) features naked girls and weak discipline:

The picture is: over here—a marching column,
Over there—a crowd.

Over here, also, is the 'Special Section' in charge of concentration camps:

There—row on row, according to years
Kolyma, Magadan,
Vorkuta and Narym
Marched in invisible columns . . .
Who and for what and by whose will—
Figure it out, History.
No bands played, no speeches;
Utter silence here.

Notch it, though it bitter be
For ever in the memory![1]

Khrushchev's dilemma is, of course, that 'de-Stalinization' has raised expectations and questions among Russians which cannot be met or answered by the present leadership. Indeed, 'Stalinism' has become a highly elastic term of abuse: a weapon whose effect depends on 'who holds it in his hands and at whom it is aimed', to paraphrase Stalin himself. In the hands of Khrushchev and his colleagues it has served to dispose of their competitors for power, at the same time advancing a case for the legitimacy of a régime which has 'unmasked the crimes of Stalin and restored Leninist principles'. In the name of de-Stalinization the present leadership has also attempted to rid the nation of certain institu-

[1] These excerpts from *Tyorkin in the Other World* translated by Leo Gruliow in *The Current Digest of the Soviet Press*, Vol. XV, No. 34, 1963.

tions and persons that prevent Russia from truly competing with the modern world, e.g. the unproductive slave labour system, and the army of incompetent bureaucrats who stand in the way of technological progress. For the liberal intelligentsia, 'Stalinism' is aimed principally at the enemies of the intellect: the dogmatist and the didact, the pharisee and the philistine whose philosophy is still nicely summed up by the official in Saltykov-Shchedrin's nineteenth century satire: 'What I do not understand is dangerous for the State'. Moreover, 'Stalinism' is for them not merely a practical but a moral issue. Konstantin Paustovsky undoubtedly spoke for the whole of the new intelligentsia when at a closed meeting of the Moscow Writers' Union in 1956 he accused the surviving Stalinist bureaucrats of 'betrayal, calumny, moral assassination and just plain assassination'. But no matter how the word is interpreted, the spirit of Stalinism—pervasive, tangible, suffocating—remains the central problem of the nation.

I remember with particular vividness the scene I witnessed once at the entrance of an auditorium where several hundred students were clamouring to be admitted to a poetry reading. Seats were evidently still available—a number of official-looking men had just been let in without question. Among the young people in the crowd was a nineteen-year-old American student of Russian from the University of Indiana. Surely this very pretty and engaging girl could have charmed her way through police lines anywhere in the world, possibly even in Tirana or Peking; here, she was faced by a barricade of boys in their twenties, the *druzhiniki* (voluntary police) with red armbands and stony faces. The Russian students had taken up her cause and lifted her over the heads of the crowd. She cajoled the *druzhiniki,* she twiddled their Komsomol badges, then, having failed, burst into tears, crying, 'But I've come all the way from Bloomington to hear Evtushenko! . . .'

Such people are everywhere in the Soviet Union: the *druzhiniki,* the vigilantes, the dreary people who are for ever denouncing their colleagues for 'adultery' or 'foul language'.

They can be spotted through the entire chain of authority from the poisonous little prig in the Young Pioneer cell, through the *Obkom* Secretary *à la* Kochetov, all the way to the Kremlin. What characterizes them is the way they hold on for dear life to every ounce or *pood* of power they possess, the cant they substitute for ordinary human discourse, and their utter disregard for other people. Indeed, of all the well-known contradictions of Soviet society none has impressed me more than the contrast between the *druzhiniki* outside the auditorium and the people at the poetry reading inside.

This poetry reading was one of a series of six I attended in the public auditorium of Moscow's Polytechnic Museum in August 1962. These began at 5 pm and, with only brief intermissions, lasted until midnight. The auditorium was filled to capacity—about 700 people, largely students from the university and from various institutes where tickets had been distributed. A majority had brought books of poetry which they followed, like music scores, during the performance. On stage, before a blue velvet backdrop on which was lettered COMMUNISM IS THE YOUTH OF THE WORLD, THEREFORE YOUTH MUST CONSTRUCT IT, sat four poets, Evtushenko, Voznesensky, Bulat Okudzhava (the immensely popular half-Georgian, half-Armenian who accompanies his poems on the guitar), and a lesser-known poet, Sergei Polikarpov.

The first to read was the twenty-nine-year-old Voznesensky. An awkward figure, slight and singularly vulnerable, he stood before the microphone with his legs stiffly apart, his Adam's apple bobbing, bearing the applause and the shouts of acclaim from the audience as if they were blows. He announced the title of his poem *Fire in the Architectural Institute*. '*Fire! Fire!*' he called out, '*Oi! We're on fire!*' This poem (which is published on p. 43) is, of course, a joke on the Academy: '*all those cowsheds decorated with cupids and those post-offices in rococo*'. It is also, I was told, a private joke shared by the audience (the Moscow Architectural Institute burned down when Voznesensky was a student there, consuming his designs together with his career as an architect).

Introduction

He read poem after poem for perhaps an hour in a powerful, cultivated voice. His awkwardness had gone; now it was
his listeners who appeared tense, straining forward to capture the flow of a language unheard-of in Russia in their
lifetime. Here, clearly, was Russia's first modern poet. A
prodigious technician, Voznesensky constructs his verse of
assonances, rhymes, and puns which serve his intention
rather as a brilliant orchestration serves a central musical
idea. ('Form isn't what counts,' he says. 'Form must be clear,
unfathomable, disquieting, like the sky in which only radar
can sense the presence of a plane.') 'I am Goya', begins one
of his most extraordinary poems whose essential quality is
not renderable in English. *'I am Goya/eye sockets of shell
craters have been picked out by an enemy/flying over a
bare field/I am sorrow/I am the voice/of war/the embers
of cities on the snows of the year '41/I am hunger/I am the
throat of a woman whose body like a bell/hangs over a
naked square . . .'* In Russian the assonances are devastating:
'*Ya Góya . . . nagóye . . . ya górye . . . ya gólos . . . góda . . .
ya gólod . . . ya górlo . . . góloi . . .*'

Most characteristic of Voznesensky's idiom are the abrupt
shifts of tone and intention within the same poem, or even
the same line; he is tender, jocular, mocking, and finally and
most compellingly, ironic. He is a master of irony and to this
end employs not only his technical resources (for example,
juxtaposing, punning, or rhyming internally a pompous word
with far-out slang) but also his alarming associations, fantasies and images, as in *The Skull Ballad* (see p. 46) where the
decapitated head of Anna Mons, the mistress of Peter the
Great, speaks to the Czar in these terms: *'love is so small
who cares for love/in times like these men build/and set a
world on fire—you kiss/me State in blood in blood.'*[1]

[1] The critic, V. Nazarenko, writing in *Zvezda*, July 1962, has made an
invidious attempt to 'decipher' this poem, and others which are part of
the cycle *The Triangular Pear*. He suggests that Voznesensky deliberately
invented the beheading of Anna Mons (she actually died a natural death)
at the so-called 'Place of Skulls' on Red Square, inserted such anachronisms
as a motor-bike, and used Soviet terminology such as *stroitelstvo* (meaning
construction, as in 'Socialist construction', in the lines quoted above which
read literally '. . . . who cares for love/in a time of construction and con-
flagration . . .') in order to 'express certain reflections of universal application'.
Nazarenko goes on to insinuate that Voznesensky is protesting against funda-
mental Marxist notions:

Even before the cultural purge released a torrent of abuse against Voznesensky, the conservative critics often accused him of 'formalism' and ambiguity. To the first charge he answered, in *Evening on the Building Site*, '*They nag me about "formalism"./Experts, what a distance/You are from life! Formalin:/You stink of it, and incense.*' And again in *Anti-Worlds*, which is a play on the concept of anti-matter, he wrote: '*Ah, my critics; how I love them./Upon the neck of the keenest of them,/Fragrant and bald as fresh-baked bread,/There shines a perfect anti-head . . .*' To the charge of ambiguity, he replied, in *Who are You?*: '*I am among avalanches/like the abominable snowman/absolutely elusive.*'

To his enemies Voznesensky is indeed elusive, but to his tremendous following he speaks more clearly than any writer in Russia. ('Here is a *real* poet,' Evtushenko said to me when he introduced me to Voznesensky during an intermission. 'He hasn't made his reputation through sensation —like some people one knows . . .') Voznesensky often talks of his responsibility to the people who have given him their confidence: 'When a man writes, he feels his prophetic mission in the world. The task of the Russian poet today is to look deep inside man. When I read my poetry to a great number of people, their emotional, almost sensual, expression of feeling seems to me to reveal the soul of man—now no longer hidden behind closed shutters, but wide open like a woman who has just been kissed.' The response to Vozne-

---

We have here, in allegorical form, gloomy reflections on the supposedly tragic fate of the individual supposedly crushed by social laws . . . on an eternal and universal scale. The message of *The Triangular Pear* is that the world is immutable and that everything will remain as it always was—that man is eternal and the tragedy of the individual is eternal.

In connexion with a cycle of poems about America, Nazarenko also insinuates that when Voznesensky writes about oppressed Negroes in America, he is actually speaking about the fate of poets in Russia. (Voznesensky's lines read: '*We are Negroes/we are poets . . . When they trample us under-foot/they are kicking the stars/the whole universe howls under your jackboots!*')

Voznesensky was promptly defended in *Literary Gazette* by the seventy-four-year-old poet Nikolai Aseyev who accused Nazarenko of making 'unseemly innuendoes' reminiscent of the Stalin era. 'This critic should remember that poets think in images,' he wrote, 'not for the sake of camouflage but because they are poets.'

sensky that evening was like nothing I have ever observed in the West, either at the theatre or in a concert hall, let alone at poetry recitals. As Voznesensky, smiling now, sweat streaming down his face like tears, was called back again and again to the footlights, I saw young men and women all around me rise and crying real tears call out their thanks.

I felt a little sorry for the poet to follow; it had to be an anti-climax. But no. Bulat Okudzhava, who appeared before the microphone cheerfully strumming a guitar, evidently inspires another sort of enthusiasm, and it broke the tension in the hall. A small dark man of thirty-seven with fuzzy, receding hair and a minute moustache, he is famous in Russia for his recordings of Odessa underworld songs (which circulate widely on tape), and for his own plaintively comic poems which he sings on public occasions in the manner of the French *chansonnier*. The audience seemed to know all his poems by heart and called for them by name: *Songs to Fools; So Long, Kid; Midnight Trolley-bus.* '*When I'm fed up/when despair comes over me/I jump into a blue trolley-bus,*' he sings pleasantly but tunelessly, '*Midnight trolley-bus! Speed along the streets/roll around the boulevards/pick up those ship-wrecked in the night . . . !*' However slight in substance, Okudzhava's little poems have charm, humour, and poignancy—qualities which appear all too rarely in Soviet literature.[1]

Recently Okudzhava has begun to write fiction. His autobiographical novella, *Good Luck, Schoolboy!*, which is excerpted in this book, suggests that the strumming of the *chansonnier* conceals more serious intentions. For Okudzhava, who was wounded at the Front, the war remains the most meaningful experience of his life. And like so many of his

[1] But not rarely enough for Ilichev. 'The Soviet people love songs,' he said in his speech of December 26, 1962, 'but side by side with songs with a broad civic motif, songs which sing the spiritual beauty of the Soviet people and reveal the purity of their souls, there are also vulgar songs which are designed to appeal to low and cheap tastes. In particular, the verse and songs of the gifted poet B. Okudzhava are out of keeping with the entire structure of our life. Their whole intonation—everything about them—does not come from purity of soul but from a kind of hysteria . . .'

generation, he is obviously weary of the hortatory tone of the majority of Soviet novels, plays and films about what is invariably called 'the heroic feat of the People in the Great Patriotic War'; these serve only to de-humanize and diminish the feat of people (with a small 'p'). Okudzhava's novella is one of the rare works of Soviet literature which deal sympathetically with the non-heroics of war—such hitherto unheard-of sentiments as the fear, bewilderment, and bravado of a teenage boy making his way across a German minefield. Inevitably the old guard critics were outraged. 'Vindication of the fear of death!' protested A. Metchenko in *Kommunist* (March 1962), 'Mawkish pacifism! Okudzhava is insulting the memory of those who died in order to save those who are living, including himself.'

The next to recite was Evtushenko. His appearance brought forth cries of 'Hi, Zhenya!' and 'Give us *Babi Yar*!' and a barrage of paper pellets on which his admirers had written requests for their favourite poems. It was clear at once that this young man's popularity is extra-literary; although Evtushenko is gifted as a poet, it is the occasional boldness of his subjects which has made his national and international reputation—especially his protest against anti-Semitism. 'Zhenya is a Columbus,' one of his enraptured admirers told me. 'He charts courses no one would dare dream of, and then everyone follows in his wake.' Moreover, he is marvellously handsome and engaging. Dressed in a wildly-patterned American sports-shirt under a grey silk suit, he brushed back his blond forelock and waved familiarly at the audience. '*Horosho*—all right, you'll have your *Babi Yar*.'

But first he read an unpublished poem: *How a Scoundrel Takes a Steambath*. This is about a detestable bureaucrat. When he goes to the public steambath he pretends to be a real friend of the people; he is always ready to scrub the back of his neighbour, and he wears a *banny list* (a leaf from the birch twigs used to beat oneself in steambaths, which sometimes gets imbedded in the skin like a burr) as an 'order of democracy'. But while lying in the hot water he sighs and pines for Stalin. And at night, before going to sleep he always treats himself to a chapter or two of Kochetov (the Stalinist novelist who is the arch enemy of the liberal writers). The next morning he resumes his villainy . . .

The audience roared with pleasure and then clamoured for *Babi Yar*. He reads it with unmistakable feeling, his arms open to the audience, his hands trembling a bit: '*Today I am as old as the Jewish people/It seems to me now that I am a Jew* . . .' When he had finished, the crowd began pounding on the floor with their feet. 'Again, at once!' He read it again, and later in the evening when the audience would not relent, read it once more. When this happened for the fourth time, Evtushenko shouted for silence and said, 'Comrades, you and I have been in this hall for six hours and I have read that poem three times. I should think you would be as tired of hearing it as I am of reciting it.' But again they pounded and once again he complied. It is a moving experience to hear this boy, so grave and so commanding, read *Babi Yar* to an audience of utterly mesmerized young Russians: '*Let the Internationale ring out/When the last anti-Semite on earth is buried./There is no Jewish blood in mine,/but I am hated by every anti-Semite as a Jew. And for this reason/I am a true Russian.*'

He also recited that evening a cycle of poems glorifying Castro's Cuba which seemed to justify the intransigent Soviet intellectuals' view that Evtushenko is deeply compromised by his concessions to the Establishment. One of these poems, *Three Minutes of Truth*, suggested why popular enthusiasm for the Cuban revolution runs so high in Russia. The poem is about a *barbudo* who seizes a radio station during the Batista régime and, for three minutes speaks 'the truth' to the people; he is then captured and shot. It ends with an exhortation by the poet who calls upon the youth of the world to remember this Cuban hero when they hear a lie: run the risk, even if it is death, but tell the truth. Evtushenko's intention may not be equivocal, but the poem, like the Cuban revolution itself, can be interpreted in more than one way. Whatever the reality of Cuba (and who in Russia can know?), for some it stands for what is most decent and pure in the revolutionary impetus; for others it means, simply, liberation from tyranny.

I saw an exhibition of Cuban painting in Moscow—the

first show entirely devoted to abstract paintings for some thirty-five years. The most interesting exhibit there was the Comment Book, where visitors are invited to note their reactions. Evtushenko, who had evidently attended the opening, had the first word: 'The Cubans have shown our respected painters that revolution and abstract art are not incompatible.' An outraged philistine wrote: 'I don't understand the pictures and I'm proud of it!' Someone replied: 'If you don't understand, go to a lunatic asylum and have your head examined!' The most touching comment: 'It is good that Cuban artists have freedom, for freedom is the beginning of everything . . .'

During an intermission, I joined Evtushenko and the other poets in a corner of the downstairs lobby. Youngsters were leaning over the whole length of the banister, obviously longing to approach their favourites for an autograph or a word of greeting. A boy of about sixteen broke away from the crowd and began walking round and round Evtushenko, frowning fiercely. Evtushenko called him over: 'What's the matter?' The boy did not answer but thrust a little volume of Evtushenko's verse at its author who signed his name in an enormous scrawl. And still the boy circled round Evtushenko. 'Come on, be happy!' said Evtushenko. The boy looked up at the poet, taller than he by a foot, and said, 'That's not enough, to be happy.' Then he added, 'Zhenya, why do you use the word communism so much in your poetry? Don't you think we're tired of all those banal slogans?' Evtushenko patted the boy on the head and told him very gently, 'Communism is my favourite word.' As I went upstairs to my seat, the boy stopped me and said, 'Zhenya is a great man—you were lucky to be able to talk with him.'

Back on stage, Evtushenko read his now-famous *The Heirs of Stalin* (see p. 219), which appeared in *Pravda* two months later (October 21 1962). For a year no editor dared touch it for the poem has a compelling message: Stalin is only feigning death; his heirs publicly curse him, privately long for his return. '*Double and triple the guards beside his grave,*' the

poet beseeches the authorities, *'lest Stalin rise again'!* Evtushenko's reading of *The Heirs of Stalin* created an extraordinary disturbance that evening. During the *disput* or
public discussion that took place following the recitations,
a young man came to the microphone and said in a quavering
voice: 'Now I like Zhenya's poetry very much. It is very
deep, very thought-provoking. But that poem about Stalin
—well—I know Stalin did some very bad things, but he also
did some very good things . . .' A fearful deafening roar
broke out in the hall. I thought the boy was about to be
lynched. Somebody's protecting hands snatched him away.

Some comic relief then presented itself on stage: a stocky,
middle-aged man, absolutely bald, with an enormous black
spade beard, and dressed in a black turtle-neck sweater and
a black serge suit. Speaking with great effort and clutching
the microphone, he introduced himself: 'I am Engineer
Dymshits.' He began speaking in short breathless phrases
which I couldn't quite catch, and I turned to my neighbour
for clarification. 'I don't get it either,' he said. But soon
the man was identified: this was the inevitable crank who
turns up in various guises at public meetings all over the
world. Engineer Dymshits works in a computer factory; he
was taking the opportunity to tell the audience, in highly
technical language, about the manufacture of adding
machines.

Most of the other speakers praised the poets warmly, until
a young Soviet army lieutenant, a good-looking blond boy
in a splendidly tailored uniform, appeared. 'I've been sitting
here for hours listening to poetry, Comrades, and I must say
I haven't the faintest idea what it's all about.' His complaint
was good-humoured. The audience snickered, rather less
good-humouredly. 'All I know is that it's very gloomy, very
depressing. Why don't you write about happy subjects—
subjects that uplift?' He was interrupted by groans and cat-
calls. 'For instance,' he persisted, 'about the Soviet army.'
Now the audience was laughing. 'Well, I'll tell you,' he
said amiably, 'if you don't take my advice and write about
the Soviet army, *we'll make you!* ' As the lieutenant was
booed off the stage, Okudzhava came to the microphone
and quieted the crowd with these words: 'Chekhov said

that it is the wise man who wants to listen and the fool who wants to teach . . .'

The last speaker, a teenage boy, came on stage with a small bunch of red roses in his hands. He addressed Sergei Polikarpov, whose pleasant but rather undistinguished poems had barely been applauded. 'No one has mentioned Polikarpov,' he said, 'and I feel very bad about it. It's not nice. Polikarpov is a good man. He is one of us. So I want to present him with these flowers and thank him on behalf of everybody in this hall.' It was the sort of small and singularly characteristic incident which, perhaps more than anything else, can endear Russia to the stranger.

After the poetry reading Evtushenko invited me to join him and some of his friends for supper. It was after midnight and every restaurant in Moscow had closed its doors, but Evtushenko persuaded the manager to let us in the back way of the restaurant of the Society of Actors. I had never seen anything like it in Moscow before. Pretty girls with beehive hairdos and green eyelids, wearing fuzzy Italian mohair sweaters over short, pleated skirts, went from table to table, greeting friends. At one table, a group of young actors in over-tailored, over-tight suits were singing *Blue Suede Shoes* in something like English. It could have been a hip Greenwich Village night club (except for a few square details, like the pair of transparent plastic shoes I glimpsed on a girl, with a single red rose imprisoned in each heel).

Evtushenko ordered several bottles of sweet Caucasian champagne and some excellent Bulgarian wine for his guests, and, as the kitchen had closed, fruit and chocolate bars. We were seven: the host, Bulat Okudzhava, a beautiful Russian singer, two modest young girls from the Moscow Art Theatre school, and Evgeni Vinokurov whom Evtushenko had summoned to the restaurant by telephone. (The thirty-seven-year-old Vinokurov, who dislikes reading in public and does not participate in literary politics, is none the less very much a part of the circle of 'young poets'.) Exhilarated by the success of the reading, Evtushenko continually pressed wine on the company and fed us bits of chocolate from hand to mouth. The singer broke out in several splendid renditions of Ella Fitzgerald songs. We drank toasts to Evtushenko, to poetry, to love. It was a gay party—and memorable, for here began a series of incidents relating to Jews as electrifying as the demonstrations I had just witnessed for *Babi Yar*.

Presently a much older man, wrapped in a flowing cape, came and sat down at our table for a time. Evtushenko hugged him and kissed him repeatedly on both cheeks. He was a poet, I was told, with an obviously Jewish name, something like Isaac Solomonovich. Evtushenko and the man sat huddled together and exchanged endearments in the Russian style. Every now and then, Evtushenko would lean across the table to me and say, 'What a wonderful man Isaac Solomonovich is—you can't imagine!' And I would say, 'Yes, I can see that—wonderful!' After several such nonsensical exchanges, Evtushenko half-rose from his chair and seized my arm. 'No!' he said, with a look of extraordinary exaltation, 'you *can't* imagine what a wonderful man Isaac Solomonovitch is,' and added, in English now, 'You can't imagine the wonderful quality of his Jewishness.' I turned to Vinokurov who was sitting beside me, plump and composed as a Buddha. He nodded: ' *Da, da, chudno! On evrei.* Yes, wonderful! He's a Jew.'

When the restaurant closed at 2.30 am, Evtushenko announced that we would all drop in on a friend who would be pleased to play host to our party. We gathered up the fruit and what remained of the wine and ambled down several streets until we reached an old-fashioned apartment house. We climbed up five flights, laughing, singing, dropping apples on the stairs, and knocked on a door which was opened by a short, dark man in his shirt sleeves. He was surprised to see us, but greeted us warmly and took us into the kitchen. On the large round table lay an open book, and on the stove, a little brass kettle with some Turkish coffee. I glanced at the book and saw that it was printed in the old pre-revolutionary Russian orthography. I turned to the title page: it was *A History of the Jewish People*, dated 1910.

We brought out the wine and fruit and continued with our party as gaily as before. After a time, I turned to the host and asked him quietly if he was Jewish. 'No, no, of course not!' he replied emphatically, and introduced himself. The name, patronymic, and surname were all typically Russian. 'Oh, well,' I fumbled, 'I thought . . . since you were reading that book . . .' 'But I am passionately interested in this question,' he said with increasing emphasis, 'aren't *you*?' I looked up and saw that everyone at the table was watching me, hard. 'Yes, I am,' I answered, and added, 'I am Jewish.' At once the guests stood and raising their glasses honoured me, in Hebrew, with that most beautiful of toasts: *Lechaim!* To life!

Lechaim! Such incidents are unlikely to occur anywhere in the world but in Soviet Russia where the use of Hebrew has always been rigorously discouraged and Jewish culture has been all but extinguished and anti-Semitism (both official and popular) continues to flourish. Since 1956, when Paustovsky was the first to accuse the old guard *apparatchiki* of anti-Semitism,[1] the liberal intellectuals have manifested their concern for Jews both publicly and privately. The novelist Victor Nekrasov, for example, protested vehemently against plans to build a sports stadium on the site of the massacre of Babi Yar. In 1962 Shostakovich composed a thirteenth Symphony whose first movement is a solo and choral recitation of Evtushenko's *Babi Yar*. As a result Shostakovich was accused, in *Soviet Culture* (December 25 1962), of 'rummaging around in the garbage cans in the backyards of our life', and Evtushenko was persuaded to delete two lines of his poem, and add two others to include Russian and Ukrainian victims of Nazism. 'The poem reveals that its author did not show political maturity,' said Khrushchev on March 8 1963, 'there is no Jewish question in our country and those who invent one echo alien voices.' The Party's assault on *Babi Yar* reflects not only its

[1] In a speech to the Moscow Writers' Union, Paustovsky (of mixed Cossack and Polish origin) described the Stalinist bureaucrats, who are, he said, 'no fewer in number than they were', in these terms: 'They are cynics, black obscurantists . . . who quite openly carry on anti-Semitic talk of a kind worthy of pogrom-makers.'

embarrassment at being taxed with anti-Semitism by 'alien voices' in the West, but also its alarm at the moral stature Evtushenko and others have assumed in the eyes of their public for their espousal of Jews. Evtushenko's changes in *Babi Yar* represent therefore a symbolic act of great importance; those who 'persuaded' him to make them no doubt understood how greatly this would discredit him with his admirers.

The intellectuals' concern for the Jews is no doubt seen as an aspect of 'abstract humanism', (of which the intellectuals are frequently accused) as distinguished from 'socialist humanism' which is, by definition, an all-embracing scheme of moral values. Increasingly the Party is reminding the people that it alone is the 'standard-bearer' of all conceivable humanist ideals and the enemy of every injustice known to man. On one point, however, the Party has long been silent: anti-Semitism in the Soviet Union. Perhaps the crowds that clamour for *Babi Yar* at poetry readings have seized upon the Jewish question because it is the one moral issue that has not been co-opted by the Party. 'Abstract humanists' may simply be persons who have become wary of any moralizing ideology which serves as a mask for oppression.

The Soviet reading public is, of course, scarcely confined to philo-Semites, anti-Stalinists, and devotees of poetry readings; there exist countless other citizens whose taste has not developed beyond the instructional rhymes and tracts which up until recently passed for literature. Today the 'scoundrels' of Evtushenko's poem, who 'pine and sigh for Stalin', have their choice of abundant bedside reading—notably, the works of Vsevolod Kochetov whose novels are printed in hundreds of thousands of copies. The nature of their appeal is obvious. Take Denisov, the hero of Kochetov's recent novel, *The Obkom Secretary*, who returns home after hearing Khrushchev's revelations of Stalin's crimes at the 20th Party Congress, and says to his wife:

'Sonya, Sonya, all our life we spent with him, life was unthinkable without him. We thought: we will die but

he will live on and on, because in him we loved Lenin. Do
you remember how he taught us to love Lenin? Do you
remember *Problems of Leninism*? . . .' Then they took out
Problems of Leninism and re-read the inspired chapters
on Vladimir Ilyich. 'Sonya, Sonya,' he said, 'in him we
loved the Party, our dear Party which brought us up, which
taught us, which armed us with an idea which made life
three times more reasonable and contented. Sonya!'

Standing in front of Stalin's photograph he says:

'No, I cannot judge him. He can be judged by the Party,
the people, history. But not by me, Vasili Denisov. Taken
separately I am too small for this. Sonya, you understand
me, don't you?' What could she reply—she cried together with him.

Kochetov's novels contain the essence of Soviet philis-
tinism. Here the enemy is nearly always the liberal intelligentsia—a band of revisionist rascals who are engaged in
subverting the work of such good Communists as Denisov.
It follows then that in real life Kochetov should be a leader
of the ultra-orthodox faction in the Writers' Union, and the
man most universally despised by the liberal writers and
their public. In April 1962, in the heyday of the liberals'
influence in literary politics, Kochetov was not even put
up for election to the board of the Moscow branch of the
Writers' Union. Yet even when the diehards seemed to
be in retreat, Kochetov managed to maintain considerable
influence as the editor of the journal *Oktyabr*, and he was
awarded the Order of Lenin in 1962 on his fiftieth birthday.
Kochetov's intransigence evidently paid off. In *Pravda* (January 1 1963), he wrote:

There is a battle of worlds going on—a cruel, irrecon-
cilable struggle between two ideologies. And now the
Party has begun to notice that on certain sectors of the
Front, in our battle for the minds of people, something
is not quite right. Certain realist artists, instead of taking
the offensive, have been forced to go on the defensive,
and instead it is the formalists and abstractionists who

have gone over to the attack. The activity of these people is alien to socialist realism because it is the spawn of the capitalist world.

Few of the liberal writers have ever had personal dealings with Kochetov. He remains utterly aloof, never appearing, I was told, at the restaurant of the Writers' Union or at any but the most official functions. Moscow journalists, Russian and foreign, have rarely encountered him. Therefore when I telephoned him for an interview I was surprised at the readiness with which he accepted. We met the following day in the boardroom of the *Oktyabr* offices. Here I had another surprise. In appearance, Kochetov is anything but the rough-and-ready proletarian his novels evoke. Except for his unpleasantly thin lips, he is a handsome man with fine features and a slim figure. He was impeccably dressed in a business-like dark suit, white shirt, and striped tie.

He greeted me most courteously, almost gratefully, it seemed. And indeed it soon became clear that Kochetov's isolation is not entirely self-imposed. During some ceremonious chit-chat early in the interview, I asked him how it happened that he was in town in August when so many Muscovites were on vacation. 'Aha! So that's why you asked to see me!' he said. 'You would never have come if other writers were in Moscow, would you?' Later, warming up a bit, he told me that journalists hardly ever visit him, 'especially women like you . . . All I see here are would-be contributors—housewives who stir *kasha* with one hand and write poetry with the other . . .'

Kochetov was eager to talk but evidently wished to say nothing. Never before had I met a man so composed in the face of disagreeable questions, and so adroit at parrying them. Only his long, beautiful fingers which drummed on the green felt-covered table between us conveyed any agitation. Even his one expression of anger sounded deliberate. '*Eto vranyo* It's a lie!' he exclaimed, when I asked him to comment on the charge that he is 'a reactionary, a Stalinist, and a baiter of intellectuals'.

'Only *Literary Gazette* and *Novy Mir* read *The Obkom Secretary* that way. I can't imagine why. All the other critics and most of my readers understood that the novel is directed against Stalinism. I even got a letter from an American woman saying that I had helped her to understand the Soviet state better by following the principles of socialist realism.' As for the charge that he is anti-intellectual, he said, 'Now let us do some arithmetic. Take my novel *The Brothers Ershov*.' He pulled out a pad of paper and made some calculations: 'I will list the negative characters first. See, there are four—all intellectuals. And here are the positive characters. Please note that there are five—all intellectuals. In other words the positive intellectuals outnumber the negative!'

I asked what he thought would happen to Soviet literature if writers were no longer expected to describe people in terms of positive and negative characters. What if socialist realism were to be abandoned and writers permitted to describe whatever reality they themselves perceive?

'It couldn't last,' he answered. 'As a matter of fact some of our writers are trying to do as you say, following the Western idea that life must be described as it is. But this is not art. It's the destruction of art. Art should certainly express truth, but only by certain means. The aim of Soviet art today must be to form the consciousness of the people while the material basis of communism is being established.' Kochetov then launched into an interminable disquisition on the Party programme for the next twenty years. Finally, returning to literature, he said, 'Only great art that educates and uplifts is genuinely loved by the great mass of people.' I observed that in the West great art of any sort usually takes some time to be understood by the great mass of people, and that unfortunately most people seem to prefer what is most vulgar in our culture. 'When you talk about vulgarity,' he said, 'I suppose you mean someone like me . . .'

Here, clearly, was a profoundly embittered man. When he spoke about his early life I began to sense the private passions engaged in his battle against the new intelligentsia. Kochetov is the youngest of eight children, all but three of whom died of hunger or typhoid fever during the First

World War. His parents, poor peasants, were unable to care for him, and he left home in Novgorod very young. He had only seven years of formal education before he went to work at unskilled jobs in various plants; later, during the first years of collectivization, he became an agronomist, then director of a Machine Tractor Station, and ultimately of a State farm. He began writing only during the Second World War when he became a military correspondent for the Leningrad *Pravda*.

Kochetov made it the hard way, and his novels are paeans to the proletariat, to men of his own experience. What can such a man feel about the young writers who have recently risen to fame by way of no harder school than the Gorky Literary Institute? I put it to him, and he replied: 'This one writes rubbish . . . that one has no ideas . . . he is also a fraud . . . not worth speaking about.' As for modern painters he observed: 'I don't know a single person in Russia, but Ehrenburg, who sees anything in abstract art. Take the exhibition of painting at the American fair in Moscow. It was a hall of laughter . . . Of course, you are probably just getting to that phase of art now. We went through it and rejected it long ago . . .'

And what about Pasternak? I heard rumours in Moscow that *Dr Zhivago* might soon be published. 'I would never want to see that book appear in its present form,' he said. 'It reminds me of some of the novels published abroad after the revolution by White Russians who were sorry they couldn't continue to live as before.' Which novels? I asked. But Kochetov did not remember. 'For me, as for the majority of Soviet citizens, the revolution is sacred. What would be your attitude towards a writer like Pasternak who described your countrymen as gangsters? . . . But, of course, you foreigners think that *Dr Zhivago* is wonderful—those who have read it and those who haven't. I can tell you that it is very badly written, although in translation it probably reads better. The language is simply awful and the whole thing is *vranyo*—a lie.'

At this point I excused myself. We had been talking for nearly four hours and I was wearied by the hatred in the man, and by the pity I somehow felt for him. We shook hands in the corridor, and he put his hand on my shoulder and said, 'You see, I'm not quite so bad as you imagined, am I? Please tell your readers that I don't eat people, that I don't swallow babies in one gulp!'

That evening I had dinner with a group of young intellectuals. I told them about my interview with Kochetov and quoted his final remark. One of the boys said, 'It's not true. He *does* eat people. And he must be awfully hungry after four hours of just talking . . .'

If Kochetov is the demon of the liberal intelligentsia, Pasternak is their saint. *'They bore him to no entombment/they bore him to enthronement,'* reads Voznesensky's poem to Pasternak (see p. 144). Nearly every young poet or writer I met in Moscow spoke of him with reverence. Hundreds of young people go every week-end to the churchyard in Peredelkino where he is buried under three tall pines. There is a bench facing the grave where they sit reading his verse (or their own) to one another. In the summer great masses of cut flowers—lilacs, roses, daisies—lie beside the grave covered over with purple pansies. Voznesensky calls it 'the most serene and beautiful place in the world . . .'

How widespread is the cult of Pasternak was illustrated for me by an incident I witnessed in a large Moscow bookshop where a famous Armenian poet, Ashot Grashi, was about to give a recitation of his poems, in connection with a book of Russian translations of his work which had just been published. The reading had not been announced; shoppers who happened to be in the store were simply being invited by the personnel to sit down on folding chairs in the poetry section. Grashi, an amiable-looking man with a great shock of black hair, then read a poem in his own language, and two or three in Russian translation to about fifty shoppers of all ages who evidently had had other plans for the afternoon. I was distressed by their bad manners: some shuffled their feet, others sighed loudly. Even the salesgirls behind the counters chattered on. The applause was perfunctory. Grashi then introduced another amiable-looking man to the audience as the translator of his poetry into

Russian, 'the man to whom I owe so much . . . etc.' The audience scarcely grew more attentive. Then the translator announced that he would read one Grashi poem 'translated not by myself, but by Boris Leonidovich Pasternak'. The whole audience rose and applauded, in cadence, for a very long time. They listened to his reading of the Pasternak translation in silence, and rose again when he had finished. Grashi then stood up, applauded, and then read it to them himself.

What can Pasternak mean to a cross-section of casual browsers in a bookshop? Pride in a man who never compromised himself or his art under Stalin? Identification or sympathy with his suffering? Genuine appreciation for his poetry? For the young writers, at any rate, he signifies all this and more. He is central to one of their most pressing concerns as writers, which is to recreate their own past. Pasternak's forty-seven years of creative work, from 1913 to 1960, bridging as it does the sterile years of Stalinism, represent their link to their literary past. As one writer put it: 'Unless we can re-live our life-story which has been denied us until now, we simply cannot get on with our work.' The writers are straining to establish some continuity with their past—not back to the nineteenth century with which they are already surfeited—but to the very point at which their literary history was arrested. By way of Pasternak (and Anna Akhmatova as well) they are returning to the masters that are rightfully theirs: Blok, Gumilev, Tsvetayeva, Khlebnikov, Mandelshtam, and, in prose, Babel and Olesha. 'Heredity,' says Voznesensky, 'can sometimes skip a generation.'

For this reason the memoirs of such older writers as Paustovsky and Ehrenburg have aroused among the younger generation an interest quite out of proportion to their documentary value. Yet their evocation of the creative excitement of a period until recently obliterated from history, and their intimate recollections of writers, like Babel and Mandelshtam, long dead in prison, are precious materials for the re-creation of the past. The Ehrenburg memoirs, however, have been received equivocally. Hardly any modern Soviet writer, let alone a painter, would deny the important role Ehrenburg has played in restoring some part of the literature and painting of the 1910's and 1920's to Russia. Yet the general feeling among the liberal intelligentsia is that the Ehrenburg memoirs, with their omissions and distortions, have once again cheated them of their history. 'I have told the truth,' Ehrenburg himself said to me in Moscow, 'but not the whole truth.'

The return to the past is no sentimental journey. What the writers are seeking is a point of departure from which they can proceed to their principal task: to resurrect the language; to restore to words the burden of meaning which has been corrupted by what Pasternak called 'the power of the glittering phrase'. Not only have such abstract nouns as freedom, justice, and truth been debased, but the language of life itself was extinguished; this is the most terrible of the indictments contained in *Dr. Zhivago*. One young poet in Moscow quoted to me from memory Yuri Zhivago's reflection on the sovereignty of language:

Language, the home and dwelling of beauty and meaning, itself begins to think and speak for man . . . then like the current of a mighty river polishing stones and turning wheels by its very movement, the flow of speech creates in passing, by the force of its own laws, rhyme and rhythm and countless other forms and formations, still more important and until now undiscovered, unconsidered, and unnamed.

There is no genuine writer in Russia today who is not dedicated to establishing the sovereignty of language over the tyranny of cant.

This is, of course, a task which strikes at the very essence of despotism. Those committed to it have been invested with a moral authority by people of conscience in Russia who have ceased to attend to the 'glittering phrase', turning instead to the language of symbol and fantasy for the truths they seek. This is why the rulers of Russia feel compelled to dictate, not only the subject matter of literature, but the means of the writer's craft as well. This is why they have repeatedly tried to lure the writers into the Establishment, hoping thereby to capture them, together with their moral authority. Failing this, they have from time to time attempted to destroy—not their persons—but their honour. And indeed, they can humiliate them before the nation. They can disperse and silence them. But one thing they cannot do: obliterate the words writers have spoken in Russia for nearly a decade. 'What has been written with a pen,' goes the Russian proverb, 'cannot be hacked away with an axe.'

'Who knows—perhaps our generation is to be sacrificed?' Evtushenko has said. 'We would then be like Napoleon's cavalrymen who threw themselves into the river to form a bridge over which others might cross to the opposite shore.'

PATRICIA BLAKE

Eight Poems

Parabolic Ballad

ANDREI VOZNESENSKY

Along a parabola life like a rocket flies,
Mainly in darkness, now and then on a rainbow.
Red-headed bohemian Gauguin the painter
Started out life as a prosperous stockbroker.
In order to get to the Louvre from Montmartre
He made a detour all through Java, Sumatra,
Tahiti, the Isles of Marquesas.
        With levity
He took off in flight from the madness of money,
The cackle of women, the frowst of academies,
Overpowered the force of terrestrial gravity.
The high priests drank their porter and kept up their jabbering:
'Straight lines are shorter, less steep than parabolas.
It's more proper to copy the heavenly mansions.'

He rose like a howling rocket, insulting them
With a gale that tore off the tails of their frock-coats.
So he didn't steal into the Louvre by the front door
But on a parabola smashed through the ceiling.
In finding their truths lives vary in daring:
Worms come through holes and bold men on parabolas.

There once was a girl who lived in my neighbourhood.
We went to one school, took exams simultaneously.
But I took off with a bang,
        I went whizzing
Through the prosperous double-faced stars of Tiflis.

Forgive me for this idiotic parabola.
Cold shoulders in a pitch-dark vestibule . . .
Rigid, erect as a radio antenna-rod
Sending its call-sign out through the freezing
Dark of the universe, how you rang out to me,
An undoubtable signal, an earthly stand-by
From whom I might get my flight-bearings to land by.
The parabola doesn't come to us easily.

Laughing at law with its warnings and paragraphs
Art, love and history race along recklessly
Over a parabolic trajectory.

He is leaving tonight for Siberia.
                    Perhaps
A straight line after all is the shorter one actually.

translated by W. H. Auden

Every railway station . . .

EVGENI VINOKUROV

Every railway station keeps a book for complaints
And, if you ask for it, they have to give it you:
It wouldn't be a bad idea, I think,
If eternity had a book like that,
Then people wouldn't have to keep silent about their sorrow.
Timidly, cautiously at first, they would all come, bringing
The griefs they endure, the wrongs they are made to suffer,
To universal attention and judgement.
How we should then be struck, I know,
By one entry of half a line
                    written
By that woman who, slumped against its railings,
Was crying in the park last night.

translated by W. H. Auden

Volcanoes

BELLA AKHMADULINA

Extinct volcanoes are silent:
Ash chokes crater and vent.
There giants hide from the sun
After the evil they have done.

Realms ever denser and colder
Weigh on each brutal shoulder,
But the old wicked visions keep
Visiting them in their sleep.

They behold a city, sure
Here summer will endure,
Though columns carved from congealed
Lava frame garden and field.

It is long ago: in sunlit hours
Girls gather armfuls of flowers
And Bacchantes give a meaning sign
To men as they sip their wine.

A feast is in progress: louder
The diners grow, more heated and lewder . . .
O my Pompei in your cindery grave,
Child of a princess and a slave!

What future did you assume,
What were you thinking of and whom
When you leaned your elbow thus
Thoughtlessly on Vesuvius?

Were you carried away by his stories?
Did you gaze with astonished eyes?
Didn't you guess—were you *that* innocent?—
Passion can be violent?

And then, when that day ended,
Did he lay a knowing forehead
At your dead feet? Did he, didn't he,
Bellow: 'Forgive me!'?

translated by W. H. Auden

Fire in the Architectural Institute

ANDREI VOZNESENSKY

Fire in the Architectural Institute!
through all the rooms and over the blueprints
like an amnesty through the jails . . .
Fire! Fire!

High on the sleepy façade
shamelessly, mischievously
like a red-assed baboon
a window skitters.

We'd already written our theses,
the time had come for us to defend them.
They're crackling away in a sealed cupboard:
all those bad reports on me!

The drafting paper is wounded,
it's a red fall of leaves;
my drawing-boards are burning,
whole cities are burning.

Five summers and five winters shoot up in flames
like a jar of kerosene.
Karen, my pet,
Oi! we're on fire!

43

Farewell architecture:
it's down to a cinder
for all those cowsheds decorated with cupids
and those post-offices in rococo!

O youth, phoenix, ninny,
your dissertation is hot stuff,
flirting its little red skirt now,
flaunting its little red tongue.

Farewell life in the sticks!
Life is a series of burned-out sites.
Nobody escapes the bonfire:
if you live—you burn.

But tomorrow, out of these ashes,
more poisonous than a bee
your compass-point will dart
to sting you in the finger.

Everything's gone up in smoke,
and there's no end of people sighing.
It's the end?
         It's only the beginning.
Let's go to the movies!

translated by Stanley Kunitz

Autumn

ANDREI VOZNESENSKY

The flapping of ducks' wings.
And on the pathways in the parks
the shimmer of the last cobwebs
and of the last bicycle spokes.

Eight Poems

You should listen to what they are hinting:
go knock at the door of the last house for leavetaking;
in that proper house a woman lives
who does not expect a husband for supper.

She will release the bolt for me
and nuzzle against my coat,
she will laugh as she offers her lips to me;
and suddenly, gone limp, she will understand everything—
the autumn call of the fields,
the scattering of seed in the wind, the breakup of families . . .

Still young, trembling with cold,
she will think about how
even the apple-tree bears fruit
and the old brown cow has a calf

and how life ferments in the hollows of oaks,
in pastures, in houses, in windswept woods,
ripening with the grain, treading with woodcocks,
and she will weep, sick with desire,

whispering, 'What good are they to me:
my hands, my breasts? What sense does it make
to live as I do, lighting the stove,
repeating my daily round of work?'

And I shall embrace her—
I who can't make sense of it either—
while outside, in the first hoarfrost,
the fields turn aluminium.
Across them—black across them—black and grey
my foot-prints will march
to the railway station.

translated by Stanley Kunitz

45

The Skull Ballad

A Digression into the seventeenth century

ANDREI VOZNESENSKY

The peasants flock from miles around
To gape at the terrible Czar
And jeer and spit at his spying bitch,
That dirty foreigner.

The Czar is skinny as a nag
And black as anthracite;
His eyes slide over his coal-black face
Like a skidding motor-bike.

Her head rolls from the blow of his axe
To the toe of his hunter's boot;
He dangles it high above the crowd
Like a red-topped turnip root.

He grips her cheeks in an iron vice,
He cracks the bridge of her nose;
The blood spurts from her golden throat
On her executioner's clothes.

He kisses her full upon the mouth,
While a groan sweeps through the crowd,
And suddenly silence stuns the square
As the death's-head speaks aloud:

   'Beloved one O worshipful Czar
   I will not judge thy guilt
   But why do thy hands stick to my skin
   and taste of my own heart's salt

let me confess my womanhood
my crime deserves the whip
I tremble where that crimson fleck
hangs on thy bristling lip

love is so small who cares for love
in times like these men build
and set a world on fire—you kiss
me State in blood in blood

what if you reek of borscht and peas
such passion has a flavour
Progress you drive me mad for you
I want you to rule for ever'

Stockstill the greatest of the Czars
Stood black as blackest bread;
A witness from abroad jerked back
Like a spike rammed to its head.

translated by Stanley Kunitz

Anti-worlds

ANDREI VOZNESENSKY

The clerk Bukashkin is our neighbour.
His face is grey as blotting-paper.

But like balloons of blue or red,
Bright Anti-Worlds
                    float over his head!
On them reposes, prestidigitous,
Ruling the cosmos, a demon-magician,
Anti-Bukashkin the Academician,
Lapped in the arms of Lollobrigidas.

But Anti-Bukashkin's dreams are the colour
Of blotting-paper, and couldn't be duller.

Long live Anti-Worlds! They rebut
With dreams the rat-race and the rut.
For some to be clever, some must be boring.
No deserts? No oases, then.

There are no women—
                    just anti-men.
In the forests, anti-machines are roaring.
There's the dirt of the earth, as well as the salt.
If the earth broke down, the sun would halt.

Ah, my critics; how I love them.
Upon the neck of the keenest of them,
Fragrant and bald as fresh-baked bread,
There shines a perfect anti-head . . .

. . . I sleep with windows open wide;
Somewhere a falling star invites,
And skyscrapers
                    like stalactites
Hang from the planet's underside.
There, upside down,
                    below me far,
Stuck like a fork into the earth,
Or perching like a carefree moth,
My little Anti-World,
                    there you are!

In the middle of the night, why is it
That Anti-Worlds are moved to visit?

Why do they sit together, gawking
At the television, and never talking?

Neither can understand a word.
How can they bear it? It's too absurd.

48

Neither can manage the least *bon ton.*
Oh, how they'll blush for it, later on!

Their ears are burning like a pair
Of crimson butterflies, hovering there . . .

. . . A distinguished lecturer lately told me,
'Anti-Worlds are a total loss.'

Still, my apartment-cell won't hold me.
I thrash in my sleep, I turn and toss.

And, radio-like, my cat lies curled
With his green eye tuned in to the world.

translated by Richard Wilbur

Foggy Street

ANDREI VOZNESENSKY

The air is grey-white as a pigeon-feather.
      Police bob up like corks on a fishing-net.
Foggy weather.
What century is it? What era? I forget.

As in a nightmare, everything is crumbling;
      people have come unsoldered; nothing's intact . . .
I plod on, stumbling—
Or flounder in cotton wool, to be more exact.

Noses. Parking lights. Badges flash and blur.
      All's vague, as at a magic-lantern show.
Your hat-check, Sir?
Mustn't walk off with the wrong head, you know.

49

Half-way to the Moon

It's as if a woman who's scarcely left your lips
        Should blur in the mind, yet trouble it with recall—
Bereft now, widowed by your love's eclipse—
        Still yours, yet suddenly not yours at all . . .

Can that be Venus? No—an ice-cream vendor!
        I bump into curbstones, bump into passers-by . . .
Are they friends, I wonder?
Home-bred Iagos, how covert you are, how sly!

Why, it's you, my darling, shivering there alone!
        Your overcoat's too big for you, my dear.
But why have you grown
That moustache? Why is there frost in your hairy ear!

I trip. I stagger. I persist.
        Murk, murk . . . there's nothing visible anywhere.
Whose is the cheek you brush now in the mist?
Ahoy there!
One's voice won't carry in this heavy air . . .

When the fog lifts, how brilliant it is, how rare!

        translated by Richard Wilbur

NOTE ON TRANSLATIONS

The translations by W. H. Auden, Stanley Kunitz, and Richard Wilbur were done in close collaboration with Max Hayward, in an attempt to overcome the difficulties of translating poetry from less well-known languages such as Russian. The editors feel that these versions, which are faithful to the sense of the originals, as well as being English poems in their own right, show beyond any doubt that the collaboration between poets who do not know the original language, and a scholar who does, can be remarkably fruitful.

Matryona's Home

ALEXANDER SOLZHENITSYN

A HUNDRED AND FIFTEEN miles from Moscow trains were still slowing down to a crawl a good six months after it happened. Passengers stood glued to the windows or went out to stand by the doors. Was the line under repair, or what? Would the train be late?

It was all right. Past the crossing the train picked up speed again and the passengers went back to their seats.

Only the engine-drivers knew what it was all about.

The engine-drivers and I.

In the summer of 1953 I was coming back from the hot and dusty desert, just following my nose—so long as it led me back to European Russia. Nobody waited or wanted me at any particular place, because I was a little matter of ten years overdue. I just wanted to get to the central belt, away from the great heats, close to the leafy muttering of forests. I wanted to efface myself, to lose myself in deepest Russia . . . if it was still anywhere to be found.

A year earlier I should have been lucky to get a job carrying a hod this side of the Urals. They wouldn't have taken me as an electrician on a decent construction job. And I had an itch to teach. Those who knew told me that it was a waste of money buying a ticket, that I should have a journey for nothing.

But things were beginning to move. When I went up the stairs of the N——Regional Education Department and asked for the Personnel Section, I was surprised to find Personnel sitting behind a glass partition, like in a chemist's shop, in-

stead of the usual black leather-padded door. I went timidly
up to the window, bowed, and asked, 'Please, do you need
any mathematicians somewhere where the trains don't run?
I should like to settle there for good.'

They passed every dot and comma in my documents
through a fine comb, went from one room to another, made
telephone calls. It was something out of the ordinary for
them too—people always wanted the towns, the bigger the
better. And lo and behold, they found just the place for
me—Vysokoe Polye [High Field]. The very sound of it
gladdened my heart.

Vysokoe Polye did not belie its name. It stood on rising
ground, with gentle hollows and other little hills around it.
It was enclosed by an unbroken ring of forest. There was a
pool behind a weir. Just the place where I wouldn't mind
living and dying. I spent a long time sitting on a stump in a
coppice and wishing with all my heart that I didn't need
breakfast and dinner every day but could just stay here and
listen to the branches brushing against the roof in the night,
with not a wireless anywhere to be heard and the whole
world silent.

Alas, nobody baked bread in Vysokoe Polye. There was
nothing edible on sale. The whole village lugged its vic-
tuals in sacks from the big town.

I went back to Personnel Section and raised my voice in
prayer at the little window. At first they wouldn't even talk
to me. But then they started going from one room to another,
made a telephone call, scratched with their pens, and
stamped on my orders the word '*Torfoprodukt*' [Peat product].

Torfoprodukt? Turgenev never knew that you can put
words like that together in Russian.

On the station building at Torfoprodukt, an antiquated
temporary hut of grey wood, hung a stern notice, BOARD
TRAINS ONLY FROM THE PASSENGERS' HALL. A further message had been scratched on the boards with a nail, *And
Without Tickets*. And by the booking-office, with the same
melancholy wit, somebody had carved for all time the words,
No Tickets. It was only later that I fully appreciated the

meaning of these addenda. Getting to Torfoprodukt was easy. But not getting away.

Here too, deep and trackless forests had once stood, and were still standing after the Revolution. Then they were chopped down by the peat-cutters and the neighbouring kolkhoz. Its chairman, Shashkov, had razed quite a few hectares of timber and sold it at a good profit down in Odessa region.

The workers' settlement sprawled untidily among the peat bogs—monotonous shacks from the 30's, and little houses with carved façades and glass verandas, put up in the 50's. But inside these houses I could see no partitions reaching up to the ceilings, so there was no hope of renting a room with four real walls.

Over the settlement hung smoke from the factory chimney. Little locomotives ran this way and that along narrow-gauge railway lines, giving out more thick smoke and piercing whistles, pulling loads of dirty brown peat in slabs and briquettes. I could safely assume that in the evening a loudspeaker would be crying its heart out over the door of the club and there would be drunks roaming the streets and, sooner or later, sticking knives in each other.

This was what my dream about a quiet corner of Russia had brought me to . . . when I could have stayed where I was and lived in an adobe hut looking out on the desert, with a fresh breeze at night and only the starry dome of the sky overhead.

I couldn't sleep on the station bench, and as soon as it started getting light I went for another stroll round the settlement. This time I saw a tiny market-place. Only one woman stood there at that early hour, selling milk, and I took a bottle and started drinking it on the spot.

I was struck by the way she talked. Instead of a normal speaking voice she used an ingratiating sing-song, and her words were the ones I was longing to hear when I left Asia for this place.

'Drink, and God bless you. You must be a stranger round here?'

'And where are you from?' I asked, feeling more cheerful.

I learnt that the peat workings weren't the only thing,

that over the railway lines there was a hill, and over the hill
a village, that this village was Talnovo, and it had been
there ages ago, when the 'gipsy woman' lived in the big
house and the wild woods stood all round. And farther on
there was a whole countryside full of villages—Chaslitsy,
Ovintsy, Spudni, Shevertni, Shestimirovo, deeper and deeper
into the woods, farther and farther from the railway, up
towards the lakes.

The names were like a soothing breeze to me. They held
a promise of backwoods Russia. I asked my new acquaintance
to take me to Talnovo after the market was over, and find a
house for me to lodge in.

It appeared that I was a lodger worth having: in addition
to my rent, the school offered a lorry-load of peat for the
winter to whoever took me. The woman's ingratiating smile
gave way to a thoughtful frown. She had no room herself,
because she and her husband were 'keeping' her aged
mother, so she took me first to one lot of relatives then to
another. But there wasn't a separate room to be had and
both places were crowded and noisy.

We had come to a dammed-up stream that was short of
water and had a little bridge over it. No other place in all
the village took my fancy as this did: there were two or
three willows, a lop-sided house, ducks swimming on the
pond, geese shaking themselves as they stepped out of the
water.

'Well, perhaps we might just call on Matryona,' said my
guide, who was getting tired of me by now. 'Only it isn't so
neat and cosy-like in her house, neglects things she does.
She's unwell.'

Matryona's house stood quite near by. Its row of four windows looked out on the cold backs, the two slopes of the roof
were covered with shingles, and a little attic window was
decorated in the old Russian style. But the shingles were
rotting, the beam-ends of the house and the once mighty
gates had turned grey with age, and there were gaps in the
little shelter over the gate.

The small door let into the gate was fastened, but instead

of knocking my companion just put her hand under and turned the catch, a simple device to prevent animals from straying. The yard was not covered, but there was a lot under the roof of the house. As you went through the outer door a short flight of steps rose to a roomy landing, which was open to the roof high overhead. To the left, other steps led up to the top room, which was a separate structure with no stove, and yet another flight down to the basement. To the right lay the house proper, with its attic and its cellar.

It had been built a long time ago, built sturdily, to house a big family, and now one lonely woman of nearly sixty lived in it.

When I went into the cottage she was lying on the Russian stove under a heap of those indeterminate dingy rags which are so precious to a working man or woman.

The spacious room, and especially the best part near the windows, was full of rubber plants in pots and tubs standing on stools and benches. They peopled the householder's loneliness like a speechless but living crowd. They had been allowed to run wild, and they took up all the scanty light on the north side. In what was left of the light, and half-hidden by the stove-pipe, the mistress of the house looked yellow and weak. You could see from her clouded eyes that illness had drained all the strength out of her.

While we talked she lay on the stove face downwards, without a pillow, her head towards the door, and I stood looking up at her. She showed no pleasure at getting a lodger, just complained about the wicked disease she had. She was just getting over an attack; it didn't come upon her every month, but when it did, 'It hangs on two or three days so as I shan't manage to get up and wait on you. I've room and to spare, you can live here if you like.'

Then she went over the list of other housewives with whom I should be quieter and cosier, and wanted me to make the round of them. But I had already seen that I was destined to settle in this dimly lit house with the tarnished mirror in which you couldn't see yourself, and the two garish posters (one advertising books, the other about the harvest), bought for a rouble each to brighten up the walls.

Matryona Vasilyevna made me go off round the village again, and when I called on her the second time she kept trying to put me off, 'We're not clever, we can't cook, I don't know how we shall suit . . .' But this time she was on her feet when I got there, and I thought I saw a glimmer of pleasure in her eyes to see me back. We reached agreement about the rent and the load of peat which the school would deliver.

Later on I found out that, year in year out, it was a long time since Matryona Vasilyevna had earned a single rouble. She didn't get a pension. Her relatives gave her very little help. In the kolkhoz she had worked not for money but for credits; the marks recording her labour days in her well-thumbed work-book.

So I moved in with Matryona Vasilyevna. We didn't divide the room. Her bed was in the corner between the door and the stove, and I unfolded my camp-bed by one window and pushed Matryona's beloved rubber plants out of the light to make room for a little table by another. The village had electric light, laid on back in the 20's, from Shatury. The newspapers were writing about 'Ilyich's little lamps,' but the peasants talked wide-eyed about 'Tsar Light'.

Some of the better-off people in the village might not have thought Matryona's house much of a home, but it kept us snug enough that autumn and winter. The roof still held the rain out, and the freezing winds could not blow the warmth of the stove away all at once, though it was cold by morning, especially when the wind blew on the shabby side.

In addition to Matryona and myself, a cat, some mice, and some cockroaches lived in the house.

The cat was no longer young, and gammy-legged as well. Matryona had taken her in out of pity, and she had stayed. She walked on all four feet but with a heavy limp: one of her feet was sore and she favoured it. When she jumped from the stove she didn't land with the soft sound a cat usually makes, but with a heavy thud as three of her feet struck the floor at once—such a heavy thud that until I got used to it, it gave me a start. This was because she stuck three feet out together to save the fourth.

It wasn't because the cat couldn't deal with them that there were mice in the cottage: she would pounce into the corner like lightning, and come back with a mouse between her teeth. But the mice were usually out of reach because somebody, back in the good old days, had stuck embossed wallpaper of a greenish colour on Matryona's walls, and not just one layer of it but five. The layers held together all right, but in many places the whole lot had come away from the wall, giving the room a sort of inner skin. Between the timber of the walls and the skin of wallpaper the mice had made themselves runs where they impudently scampered about, running at times right up to the ceiling. The cat followed their scamperings with angry eyes, but couldn't get at them.

Sometimes the cat ate cockroaches as well, but they made her sick. The only thing the cockroaches respected was the partition which screened the mouth of the Russian stove and the kitchen from the best part of the room.

They did not creep into the best room. But the kitchen at night swarmed with them, and if I went in late in the evening for a drink of water and switched on the light the whole floor, the big bench, and even the wall would be one rustling brown mass. From time to time I brought home some borax from the school laboratory and we mixed it with dough to poison them. There would be fewer cockroaches for a while, but Matryona was afraid that we might poison the cat as well. We stopped putting down poison and the cockroaches multiplied anew.

At night, when Matryona was already asleep and I was working at my table, the occasional rapid scamper of mice behind the wallpaper would be drowned in the sustained and ceaseless rustling of cockroaches behind the screen, like the sound of the sea in the distance. But I got used to it because there was nothing evil in it, nothing dishonest. Rustling was life to them.

I even got used to the crude beauty on the poster, for ever reaching out from the wall to offer me Belinsky, Panferov,

and a pile of other books—but never saying a word. I got
used to everything in Matryona's cottage.

Matryona got up at 4 or 5 o'clock in the morning. Her
wall-clock was twenty-seven years old, and had been bought
in the village shop. It was always fast, but Matryona didn't
worry about that—just so long as it didn't lose and make
her late in the morning. She switched on the light behind
the kitchen screen and moving quietly, considerately, doing
her best not to make a noise, she lit the stove, went to milk
the goat (all the livestock she had was this one dirty-white
goat with twisted horns), fetched water and boiled it in three
iron pots: one for me, one for herself, and one for the goat.
She fetched potatoes from the cellar, picking out the littlest
for the goat, little ones for herself and egg-sized ones for me.
There were no big ones, because her garden was sandy, had
not been manured since the war and was always planted
with potatoes, potatoes, and potatoes again, so that it
wouldn't grow big ones.

I scarcely heard her about her morning tasks. I slept late,
woke up in the wintry daylight, stretched a bit and stuck
my head out from under my blanket and my sheep-skin.
These, together with the prisoner's jerkin round my legs and a
sack stuffed with straw underneath me, kept me warm in bed
even on nights when the cold wind rattled our wobbly windows
from the north. When I heard the discreet noises on the other
side of the screen I spoke to her, slowly and deliberately.

'Good morning, Matryona Vasilyevna!'

And every time the same good-natured words came to me
from behind the screen. They began with a warm, throaty
gurgle, the sort of sound grandmothers make in fairy-tales.

'M-m-m . . . same to you too!'

And after a little while, 'Your breakfast's ready for you
now.'

She didn't announce what was for breakfast, but it was
easy to guess: taters in their jackets or tatty soup (as everybody in the village called it), or barley gruel (no other grain
could be bought in Torfoprodukt that year, and even the
barley you had to fight for, because it was the cheapest and

people bought it up by the sack to fatten their pigs on it).
It wasn't always salted as it should be, it was often slightly
burnt, it furred the palate and the gums, and it gave me
heartburn.

But Matryona wasn't to blame: there was no butter in
Torfoprodukt either, margarine was desperately short, and
only mixed cooking fat was plentiful, and when I got to
know it I saw that the Russian stove was not convenient for
cooking: the cook cannot see the pots and they are not heated
evenly all round. I suppose the stove came down to our an-
cestors from the Stone Age because you can stoke it up once
before daylight, and food and water, mash and swill, will
keep warm in it all day long. And it keeps you warm while
you sleep.

I ate everything that was cooked for me without demur,
patiently putting aside anything uncalled-for that I came
across: a hair, a bit of peat, a cockroach's leg. I hadn't the
heart to find fault with Matryona. After all, she had warned
me herself,

'We aren't clever, we can't cook—I don't know how we
shall suit ...'

'Thank you,' I said quite sincerely.

'What for? For what is your own?' she answered, disarm-
ing me with a radiant smile. And, with a guileless look of
her faded-blue eyes, she would ask, 'And what shall I cook
you for just now?'

For just now meant for supper. I ate twice a day, like at
the Front. What could I order for just now? It would have
to be one of the same old things, taters or tater soup.

I resigned myself to it, because I had learnt by now not to
look for the meaning of life in food. More important to me
was the smile on her roundish face, which I tried in vain to
catch when at last I had earned enough to buy a camera.
As soon as she saw the cold eye of the lens upon her Matryona
assumed a strained or else an exaggeratedly severe expression.

Just once I did manage to get a snap of her looking through
the window into the street and smiling at something.

Matryona had a lot of worries that winter. Her neighbours put it into her head to try and get a pension. She was all alone in the world, and when she began to be seriously ill she had been dismissed from the kolkhoz as well. Injustices had piled up, one on top of another. She was ill, but not regarded as a disabled person. She had worked for a quarter of a century in the kolkhoz, but it was a kolkhoz and not a factory, so she was not entitled to a pension for herself. She could only try and get one for her husband, for the loss of her bread-winner. But she had had no husband for twelve years now, not since the beginning of the war, and it wasn't easy to obtain all the particulars from different places about his length of service and how much he had earned. What a bother it was getting those forms through! Getting somebody to certify that he'd earned, say, 300 roubles a month; that she lived alone and nobody helped her; what year she was born in. Then all this had to be taken to the Pensions Office. And taken somewhere else to get all the mistakes corrected. And taken back again. Then you had to find out whether they would give you a pension.

To make it all more difficult the Pensions Office was twelve miles east of Talnovo, the Rural Council Offices six miles to the west, the Factory District Council an hour's walk to the north. They made her run around from office to office for two months on end, to get an *i* dotted or a *t* crossed. Every trip took a day. She goes down to the Rural District Council—and the secretary isn't there today. Secretaries of rural councils often aren't here today. So come again tomorrow. Tomorrow the secretary is in, but he hasn't got his rubber stamp. So come again the next day. And the day after that back she goes yet again, because all her papers are pinned together and some cock-eyed clerk has signed the wrong one.

'They shove me around, Ignatich,' she used to complain to me after these fruitless excursions. 'Worn out with it I am.'

But she soon brightened up. I found that she had a sure means of putting herself in a good humour. She worked. She would grab a shovel and go off to lift potatoes. Or she would tuck a sack under her arm and go after peat. Or take a wicker basket and look for berries deep in the woods. When she'd been bending her back to bushes instead of office desks for a while, and her shoulders were aching from a heavy load, Matryona would come back cheerful, at peace with the world and smiling her nice smile.

'I'm on to a good thing now, Ignatich. I know where to go for it (peat she meant), a lovely place it is.'

'But surely my peat is enough, Matryona Vasilyevna? There's a whole lorry-load of it.'

'Pooh! Your peat! As much again, and then as much again, that might be enough. When the winter gets really stiff and the wind's battling at the windows, it blows the heat out of the house faster than you can make the stove up. Last year we got heaps and heaps of it. I'd have had three loads in by now. But they're out to catch us. They've summoned one woman from our village already.'

That's how it was. The frightening breath of winter was already in the air. There were forests all round, and no fuel to be had anywhere. Excavators roared away in the bogs, but there was no peat on sale to the villagers. It was delivered, free, to the bosses and to the people round the bosses, and teachers, doctors, and workers got a load each. The people of Talnovo were not supposed to get any peat, and they weren't supposed to ask about it. The chairman of the kolkhoz walked about the village looking people in the eye while he gave his orders or stood chatting, and talked about anything you liked except fuel. He was stocked-up. Who said anything about winter coming?

So just as in the old days they used to steal the squire's wood, now they pinched peat from the trust. The women went in parties of five or ten so that they would be less frightened. They went in the day-time. The peat cut during the summer had been stacked up all over the place to dry. That's the good thing about peat, it can't be carted off as soon as it's cut. It lies around drying till autumn, or, if the roads are bad, till the snow starts falling. This was when the women used to come and take it. They could get six peats in a sack if it was damp, or ten if it was dry. A sackful

weighed about half a hundredweight and it sometimes had
to be carried over two miles. This was enough to make the
stove up once. There were 200 days in the winter. The Russian
stove had to be lit in the mornings, and the 'Dutch' stove
in the evenings.

'Why beat about the bush?' said Matryona angrily to someone invisible. 'Since there've been no more horses, what you
can't heave around yourself you haven't got. My back never
heals up. Winter you're pulling sledges, summer it's bundles
on your back, it's God's truth I'm telling you.'

The women went more than once in a day. On good days
Matryona brought six sacks home. She piled my peat up
where it could be seen, and hid her own under the passageway, boarding up the hole every night.

'If they don't just happen to think of it, the devils will
never find it in their born days,' said Matryona smiling and
wiping the sweat from her brow.

What could the peat trust do? It's establishment didn't run
to a watchman for every bog. I suppose they had to show a
rich haul in their returns, and then write off so much for
crumbling, so much washed away by the rain . . . Sometimes
they would take it into their heads to put out patrols and try
to catch the women as they came into the village. The
women would drop their sacks and scatter. Or somebody
would inform and there would be a house-to-house search.
They would draw up a report on the stolen peat, and
threaten a court action. The women would stop fetching it
for a while, but the approach of winter drove them out with
sledges in the middle of the night.

When I had seen a little more of Matryona I noticed that
apart from cooking and looking after the house, she had
quite a lot of other jobs to do every day. She kept all her
jobs, and the proper times for them, in her head and always
knew when she woke up in the morning how her day would
be occupied. Apart from fetching peat, and stumps which
the tractors unearthed in the bogs, apart from the cran-
berries which she put to soak in big jars for the winter
('Give your teeth an edge, Ignatich,' she used to say when

she offered me some), apart from digging potatoes and all the coming and going to do with her pension, she had to get hay from somewhere for her one and only dirty-white goat.

'Why don't you keep a cow, Matryona?'

Matryona stood there in her grubby apron, by the opening in the kitchen screen, facing my table, and explained to me.

'Oh, Ignatich, there's enough milk from the goat for me. And if I started keeping a cow she'd eat me out of house and home in no time. You can't cut the grass by the railway track, because it belongs to the railway, and you can't cut any in the woods, because it belongs to the foresters, and they won't let me have any at the kolkholz because I'm not a member any more, they reckon. And those who are members have to work there every day till the white flies swarm, and make their own hay when there's snow on the ground— what's the good of grass like that? In the old days they used to be sweating to get the hay in at midsummer, between the end of June and the end of July, while the grass was sweet and juicy . . .'

So it meant a lot of work for Matryona to gather enough hay for one skinny little goat. She took her sickle and a sack and went off early in the morning to places where she knew there was grass growing—round the edges of fields, on the roadside, on hummocks in the bog. When she had stuffed her sack with heavy fresh grass she dragged it home and spread it out in her yard to dry. From a sackful of grass she got one forkload of dry hay.

The farm had a new chairman, sent down from the town not long ago, and the first thing he did was to cut down the garden-plots for those who were not fit to work. He left Matryona a third of an acre of sand—when there was over a thousand square yards just lying idle on the other side of the fence. Yet when they were short of working hands, when the women dug in their heels and wouldn't budge, the chairman's wife would come to see Matryona. She was from the town as well, a determined woman whose short grey overcoat and intimidating glare gave her a somewhat military appearance. She walked into the house without so much as a good morning and looked sternly at Matryona. Matryona was uneasy.

'Well now, Comrade Vasilyevna,' said the chairman's wife,

drawing out her words. 'You will have to help the kolkhoz! You will have to go and help cart muck out tomorrow!'

A little smile of forgiveness wrinkled Matryona's face—as though she understood the embarrassment which the chairman's wife must feel not being able to pay her for her work.

'Well—er,' she droned. 'I'm not well, of course, and I'm not attached to you any more . . .,' then she hurried to correct herself, 'What time should I come then?'

'And bring your own fork!' the chairman's wife instructed her. Her stiff skirt crackled as she walked away.

'Think of that!' grumbled Matryona as the door closed. 'Bring your own fork! They've got neither forks nor shovels on the kolkhoz. And I don't have a man who'll put a handle on for me!'

She went on thinking about it out loud all evening.

'What's the good of talking, Ignatich. I must help, of course. Only the way they work it's all a waste of time—don't know whether they're coming or going. The women stand propped up on their shovels and waiting for the factory hooter to blow 12 o'clock. Or else they get on to adding up who's earned what and who's turned up for work and who hasn't. Now what I call work, there isn't a sound out of anybody, only . . . oh dear, dear—dinner-time's soon rolled round— what, getting dark already . . .'

In the morning she went off with her fork.

But it wasn't just the kolkhoz—any distant relative, or just a neighbour, could come to Matryona of an evening and say, 'Come and give me a hand tomorrow, Matryona. We'll finish lifting the potatoes.'

Matryona couldn't say no. She gave up what she should be doing next and went to help her neighbour, and when she came back she would say without a trace of envy, 'Ah, you should see the size of her potatoes, Ignatich! It was a joy to dig them up. I didn't want to leave the allotment, God's truth I didn't.'

Needless to say, not a garden could be ploughed without Matryona's help. The women of Talnovo had got it neatly worked out that it was a longer and harder job for one

woman to dig her garden with a spade than for six of them
to put themselves in harness and plough six gardens. So they
sent for Matryona to help them.

'Well—did you pay her?' I asked sometimes.

'She won't take money. You have to try and hide it on her
when she's not looking.'

Matryona had yet another troublesome chore when her
turn came to feed the herdsmen. One of them was a hefty
deaf mute, the other a boy who was never without a cigarette
in his drooling mouth. Matryona's turn only came round
every six weeks, but it put her to great expense. She went
to the shop to buy tinned fish, and was lavish with sugar and
butter, things she never ate herself. It seems that the housewives showed off in this way, trying to outdo each other in
feeding the herdsmen.

'You've got to be careful with tailors and herdsmen,'
Matryona explained. 'They'll spread your name all round the
village if something doesn't suit them.'

And every now and then attacks of serious illness broke in
on this life that was already crammed with troubles. Matryona
would be off her feet for a day or two, lying flat out on the
stove. She didn't complain, and didn't groan, but she hardly
stirred either. On these days Masha, Matryona's closest
friend from her earliest years, would come to look after the
goat and light the stove. Matryona herself ate nothing, drank
nothing, asked for nothing. To call in the doctor from the
clinic at the settlement would have seemed strange in Talnovo, and would have given the neighbours something to
talk about—what does she think she is, a lady? They did
call her in once, and she arrived in a real temper and told
Matryona to come down to the clinic when she was on her
feet again. Matryona went, although she didn't really want
to; they took specimens and sent them off to the district
hospital—and that's the last anybody heard about it. Matryona was partly to blame herself.

But there was work waiting to be done, and Matryona soon
started getting up again, moving slowly at first and then as
briskly as ever.

'You never saw me in the old days, Ignatich. I'd lift any sack
you liked, I didn't think a hundredweight was too heavy. My

C

father-in-law used to say, "Matryona, you'll break your back."
And my brother-in-law didn't have to come and help me lift
on the cart. Our horse was a war-horse, a big strong one . . .'

'What do you mean, a war-horse?'

'They took ours for the war and gave us this one instead
—he'd been wounded. But he turned out a bit spirited. Once
he bolted with the sledge right into the lake, the men-folk
hopped out of the way, but I grabbed the bridle, as true as I'm
here, and stopped him . . . Full of oats that horse was. They
liked to feed their horses well in our village. If a horse feels
his oats he doesn't know what heavy means.'

But Matryona was a long way from being fearless. She
was afraid of fire, afraid of 'the lightning,' and most of all she
was for some reason afraid of trains.

'When I had to go to Cherusti the train came up from
Nechaevka way with its great big eyes popping out and the
rails humming away—put me in a proper fever. My knees
started knocking. God's truth I'm telling you!' Matryona
raised her shoulders as though she surprised herself.

'Maybe it's because they won't give people tickets, Matryona Vasilyevna?'

'At the window? They try to shove first-class tickets on to
you. And the train was starting to move. We dashed about
all over the place, "Give us tickets for pity's sake."

'The men-folk had climbed on top of the carriages. Then
we found a door that wasn't locked and shoved straight in
without tickets . . . and all the carriages were empty, they
were all empty, you could stretch out on the seat if you
wanted to. Why they wouldn't give us tickets, the hard-
hearted parasites, I don't know . . .'

Still, before winter came Matryona's affairs were in a better
state than ever before. They started paying her at last a pension of eighty roubles. Besides this she got just over 100
from the school and me.

Some of her neighbours began to be envious.

'Hm! Matryona can live for ever now! If she had any
more money she wouldn't know what to do with it at her
age.'

Matryona had herself some new felt boots made. She bought a new jerkin. And she had an overcoat made out of the worn-out railwayman's greatcoat given to her by the engine-driver from Cherusti who had married Kira, her foster-daughter. The hump-backed village tailor put a padded lining under the cloth and it made a marvellous coat, such as Matryona had never worn before in all her sixty years.

In the middle of winter Matryona sewed 200 roubles into the lining of this coat for her funeral. This made her quite cheerful.

'Now my mind's a bit easier, Ignatich.'

December went by, January went by—and in those two months Matryona's illness held off. She started going over to Masha's house more often in the evening, to sit chewing sun-flower seeds with her. She didn't invite guests herself in the evening out of consideration for my work. Once, on the feast of the Epiphany, I came back from school and found a party going on and was introduced to Matryona's three sisters who called her 'nan-nan' or 'nanny' because she was the oldest. Until then not much had been heard of the sisters in our cottage—perhaps they were afraid that Matryona might ask them for help.

But one ominous event cast a shadow on the holiday for Matryona. She went to the church three miles away for the blessing of the water, and put her pot down among the others. When the blessing was over the women went rush-ing and jostling to get their pots back again. There were a lot of women in front of Matryona and when she got there her pot was missing, and no other vessel had been left behind. The pot had vanished as though the Devil had run off with it.

Matryona went around the worshippers asking them, 'Has any of you girls accidentally mistook somebody else's holy water? In a pot?'

Nobody owned up. There had been some boys there, and boys got up to mischief sometimes. Matryona came home sad.

No one could say that Matryona was a devout believer. If anything, she was a heathen, and her strongest beliefs were superstitious: you mustn't go into the garden on the fast of St John or there would be no harvest next year. A blizzard meant that somebody had hanged himself. If you pinched your foot in the door you could expect a guest. All the time I lived with her I didn't once see her say her prayers or even cross herself. But, whatever job she was doing, she began with a 'God bless us', and she never failed to say 'God bless you', when I set out for school. Perhaps she did say her prayers, but on the quiet, either because she was shy or because she didn't want to embarrass me. There were ikons on the walls. Ordinary days they were left in darkness, but for the vigil of a great feast, or on the morning of a holiday, Matryona would light the little lamp.

She had fewer sins on her conscience than her gammy-legged cat. The cat did kill mice . . .

Now that her life was running more smoothly, Matryona started listening more carefully to my radio. (I had, of course, installed a speaker, or as Matryona called it, a peeker.)

When they announced on the radio that some new machine had been invented, I heard Matryona grumbling out in the kitchen, 'New ones all the time, nothing but new ones. People don't want to work with the old ones any more, where are we going to store them all?'

There was a programme about the seeding of clouds from aeroplanes. Matryona, listening up on the stove, shook her head, 'Oh, dear, dear, dear, they'll do away with one of the two—summer or winter.'

Once Chaliapin was singing Russian folk-songs. Matryona stood listening for a long time before she gave her emphatic verdict, 'Queer singing, not our sort of singing.'

'You can't mean that, Matryona Vasilyevna . . . just listen to him.'

She listened a bit longer, and pursed her lips, 'No, it's wrong. It isn't our sort of tune, and he's tricky with his voice.'

She made up for this another time. They were broadcasting some of Glinka's songs. After half a dozen of these drawing-room ballads, Matryona suddenly came from behind the screen clutching her apron, with a flush on her face and a film of tears over her dim eyes.

'That's our sort of singing,' she said in a whisper.

So Matryona and I got used to each other and took each other for granted. She never pestered me with questions about myself. I don't know whether she was lacking in normal female curiosity or just tactful, but she never once asked if I had been married. All the Talnovo women kept at her to find out about me. Her answer was, 'You want to know—you ask him. All I know is he's from distant parts.'

And when I got round to telling her that I had spent a lot of time in prison she said nothing but just nodded, as though she had already suspected it.

And I thought of Matryona only as the helpless old woman she was now, and didn't try to rake up her past, didn't even suspect that there was anything to be found there.

I knew that Matryona had got married before the Revolution and come to live in the house I now shared with her, that she had gone 'to the stove' immediately. (She had no mother-in-law and no older sister-in-law, so it was her job to put the pots in the oven on the very first morning of her married life.) I knew that she had had six children and that they had all died very young, so that there were never two of them alive at once. Then there was a sort of foster-daughter, Kira. Matryona's husband had not come back from the last war. She received no notification of his death. Men from the village who had served in the same company said that he might have been taken prisoner, or he might have been killed and his body not found. In the eight years that had gone by since the war Matryona had decided that he was not alive. It was a good thing that she thought so. If he was still alive he was probably in Brazil or Australia, and married again. The village of Talnovo, and the Russian language, would be fading from his memory.

One day, when I got back from school, I found a guest in the house. A tall, dark man, with his hat on his lap, was sitting on a chair which Matryona had moved up to the Dutch stove in the middle of the room. His face was completely surrounded by bushy black hair with hardly a trace of grey in it. His thick black moustaches ran into his full black beard, so that his mouth could hardly be seen. Black side-whiskers merged with the black locks which hung down from his crown, leaving only the tips of his ears visible; and broad black eyebrows met in a wide double span. But the front of his head as far as the crown was a spacious bald dome. His whole appearance made an impression of wisdom and dignity. He sat squarely on his chair, with his hands folded on his stick, and his stick resting vertically on the floor, in an attitude of patient expectation, and he obviously hadn't much to say to Matryona who was busy behind the screen.

When I came in he eased his majestic head round towards me and suddenly addressed me, 'Master, I can't see you very well. My son goes to your school. Grigoriev, Antoshka . . .'

There was no need for him to say any more . . . However strongly inclined I felt to help this worthy old man I knew and dismissed in advance all the pointless things he was going to say. Antoshka Grigoriev was a plump, red-faced lad in 8-D who looked like a cat that's swallowed the cream. He seemed to think that he came to school for a rest and sat at his desk with a lazy smile on his face. Needless to say, he never did his homework. But the worst of it was that he had been put up into the next class from year to year because our district, and indeed the whole region and the neighbouring region, were famous for the high percentage of passes they obtained, and the school had to make an effort to keep its record up. So Antoshka had got it clear in his mind that however much the teachers threatened him they would put him up in the end, and there was no need for him to learn anything. He just laughed at us. There he sat in the eighth class, and he hadn't even mastered his decimals and didn't know one triangle from another. In the first two terms of the school year I had kept him firmly below the pass line and the same treatment awaited him in the third.

But now this half-blind old man, who should have been

Antoshka's grandfather rather than his father, had come to
humble himself before me—how could I tell him that the
school had been deceiving him for years, and that I couldn't
go on deceiving him, because I didn't want to ruin the whole
class, to become a liar and a fake, to start despising my work
and my profession.

For the time being I patiently explained that his son had
been very slack, that he told lies at school and at home, that
his mark-book must be checked frequently, and that we must
both take him severely in hand.

'Severe as you like, master,' he assured me, 'I beat him
every week now. And I've got a heavy hand.'

While we were talking I remembered that Matryona had
once interceded for Antoshka Grigoriev, but I hadn't asked
what relation of hers he was and I had refused to do what she
wanted. Matryona was standing in the kitchen doorway like
a mute suppliant on this occasion too. When Faddei Mirono-
vich left saying that he would call on me to see how things
were going, I asked her, 'I can't make out what relation
this Antoshka is to you, Matryona Vasilyevna.'

'My brother-in-law's son,' said Matryona shortly, and went
out to milk the goat.

When I'd worked it out I realized that this determined old
man with the black hair was the brother of the missing
husband.

The long evening went by, and Matryona didn't bring up
the subject again. But late at night, when I had stopped
thinking about the old man and was working in a silence
broken only by the rustling of the cockroaches and the heavy
tick of the wall-clock, Matryona suddenly spoke from her
dark corner, 'You know, Ignatich, I nearly married him
once.'

I had forgotten that Matryona was in the room. I hadn't
heard a sound from her—and suddenly her voice came out
of the darkness, as agitated as if the old man were still trying
to win her.

I could see that Matryona had been thinking about nothing else all evening.

She got up from her wretched rag bed and walked slowly
towards me, as though she were following her own words. I

sat back in my chair and caught my first glimpse of a quite different Matryona.

There was no overhead light in our big room with its forest of rubber plants. The table lamp cast a ring of light round my exercise books, and when I tore my eyes from it the rest of the room seemed to be half-dark and faintly tinged with pink. I thought I could see the same pinkish glow in her usually sallow cheeks.

'He was the first one who came courting me, before Yefim did . . . he was his brother . . . the older one . . . I was nineteen and Faddei was twenty-three . . . They lived in this very same house. Their house it was. Their father built it.'

I looked round the room automatically. Instead of the old grey house rotting under the faded green skin of wallpaper where the mice had their playground, I suddenly saw new timbers, freshly trimmed, and not yet discoloured, and caught the cheerful smell of pine-tar.

'Well, and what happened then?'

'That summer we went to sit in the coppice together,' she whispered. 'There used to be a coppice where the stable-yard is now. They chopped it down . . . I was just going to marry him, Ignatich. Then the German war started. They took Faddei in the army.'

She let fall these few words—and suddenly the blue and white and yellow July of the year 1914 burst into flower before my eyes: the sky still peaceful, the floating clouds, the people sweating to get the ripe corn in. I imagined them side by side, the black-haired Hercules with a scythe over his shoulder, and the red-faced girl clasping a sheaf. And there was singing out under the open sky, such songs as nobody can sing nowadays, with all the machines in the fields.

'He went to the war—and vanished. For three years I kept to myself and waited. Never a sign of life did he give . . .'

Matryona's round face looked out at me from an elderly threadbare head-scarf. As she stood there in the gentle reflected light from my lamp her face seemed to lose its slovenly workaday covering of wrinkles, and she was a scared young girl again with a frightening decision to make.

Yes . . . I could see it . . . The trees shed their leaves, the snow fell and melted. They ploughed and sowed and reaped again. Again the trees shed their leaves, and snow fell. There was a revolution. Then another revolution. And the whole world was turned upside down.

'Their mother died and Yefim came to court me. You wanted to come to our house, he says, so come. He was a year younger than me, Yefim was. It's a saying with us—sensible girls get married after Michaelmas, and silly ones at midsummer. They were short-handed. I got married . . . The wedding was on St Peter's day, and then about St Nicolas' day in the winter he came back . . . Faddei, I mean, from being a prisoner in Hungary.'

Matryona covered her eyes.

I said nothing.

She turned towards the door as though somebody were standing there. 'He stood there at the door. What a scream I let out! I wanted to throw myself at his feet! . . . but I couldn't. If it wasn't my own brother, he says, I'd take my axe to the both of you.'

I shuddered. Matryona's despair or her terror, conjured up a vivid picture of him standing in the dark doorway and raising his axe to her.

But she quietened down and went on with her story in a sing-song voice, leaning on a chair-back, 'Oh dear, dear me, the poor dear man! There were so many girls in the village—but he wouldn't marry. I'll look for one with the same name as you, a second Matryona, he said. And that's what he did—fetched himself a Matryona from Lipovka. They built themselves a house of their own and they're still living in it. You pass their place every day on your way to school.'

So that was it. I realized that I had seen the other Matryona quite often. I didn't like her. She was always coming to my Matryona to complain about her husband—he beat her, he was stingy, he was working her to death. She would weep and weep, and her voice always had a tearful note in it. As it turned out, my Matryona had nothing to regret, with Faddei beating his Matryona every day of his life and being so tight-fisted.

'Mine never beat me once,' said Matryona of Yefim. 'He'd

C*

pitch into another man in the street, but me he never hit once . . . Well, there was one time . . . I quarrelled with my sister-in-law and he cracked me on the forehead with a spoon. I jumped up from the table and shouted at them, "Hope it sticks in your gullets, you idle lot of beggars, hope you choke!" I said. And off I went into the woods. He never touched me any more.'

Faddei didn't seem to have any cause for regret either. The other Matryona had borne him six children (my Antoshka was one of them, the littlest, the runt) and they had all lived, whereas the children of Matryona and Yefim had died, every one of them, before they reached the age of three months, without any illness.

'One daughter, Elena, was born and was alive when they washed her, and then she died right after . . . My wedding was on St Peter's day, and it was St Peter's day I buried my sixth, Alexander.'

The whole village decided that there was a curse on Matryona.

Matryona still nodded emphatic belief when she talked about it. 'There was a *course* on me. They took me to a woman as used to be a nun to get cured, she set me off coughing and waited for the *course* to jump out of me like a frog. Only nothing jumped out . . .'

And the years had run by like running water . . . In 1941 they didn't take Faddei into the army because of his poor sight, but they took Yefim. And what had happened to the elder brother in the First World War happened to the younger in the Second . . . he vanished without trace. Only he never came back at all. The once noisy cottage was deserted, it became old and rotten, and Matryona, all alone in the world, grew old in it.

So she begged from the other Matryona, the cruelly beaten Matryona, a child of her womb (or was it a spot of Faddei's blood?), the youngest daughter, Kira.

For ten years she brought the girl up in her own house, in place of the children who had not lived. Then, not long before I arrived, she had married her off to a young engine-driver from Cherusti. The only help she got from any-where came in dribs and drabs from Cherusti: a bit of sugar from time to time, or some of the fat when they killed a pig.

Sick and suffering, and feeling that death was not far off, Matryona had made known her will: the top room, which was a separate frame joined by tie-beams to the rest of the house, should go to Kira when she died. She said nothing about the house itself. Her three sisters had their eyes on it too.

That evening Matryona opened her heart to me. And, as often happens, no sooner were the hidden springs of her life revealed to me than I saw them in motion.

Kira arrived from Cherusti. Old Faddei was very worried. To get and keep a plot of land in Cherusti the young couple had to put up some sort of building. Matryona's top-room would do very well. There was nothing else they could put up, because there was no timber to be had anywhere. It wasn't Kira herself so much, and it wasn't her husband, but old Faddei who was consumed with eagerness for them to get their hands on the plot at Cherusti.

He became a frequent visitor, laying down the law to Matryona and insisting that she should hand over the top room right away, before she died. On these occasions I saw a different Faddei. He was no longer an old man propped up by a stick, whom a push or a harsh word would bowl over. Although he was slightly bent by back-ache, he was still a fine figure; he had kept the vigorous black hair of a young man in his sixties; he was hot and urgent.

Matryona had not slept for two nights. It wasn't easy for her to make up her mind. She didn't grudge them the top room, which was standing there idle, any more than she ever grudged her labour or her belongings. And the top room was willed to Kira in any case. But the thought of breaking up the roof she had lived under for forty years was torture to her. Even I, a mere lodger, found it painful to think of them stripping away boards and wrenching out beams. For Matryona it was the end of everything.

But the people who were so insistent knew that she would let them break up her house before she died.

So Faddei and his sons and sons-in-law came along one February morning, the blows of five axes were heard and boards creaked and cracked as they were wrenched out. Faddei's eyes twinkled busily. Although his back wasn't quite straight yet he scrambled nimbly up under the rafters and bustled about down below, shouting at his assistants. He and his father had built this house when he was a lad, a long time ago. The top room had been put up for him, the oldest son, to move in with his bride. And now he was furiously taking it apart, board by board, to carry it out of somebody else's yard.

After numbering the beam-ends and the ceiling boards they dismantled the top room and the store-room underneath it. The living-room, and what was left of the landing, they boarded up with a thin wall of deal. They did nothing about the cracks in the wall. It was plain to see that they were wreckers, not builders, and that they did not expect Matryona to be living there very long.

While the men were busy wrecking, the women were getting the drink ready for moving day—vodka would cost a lot too much. Kira brought forty pounds of sugar from Moscow region, and Matryona carried the sugar and some bottles to the distiller under cover of night.

The timbers were carried out and stacked in front of the gates, and the engine-driver son-in-law went off to Cherusti for the tractor.

But the very same day a blizzard, or 'a blower' as Matryona called it, began. It howled and whirled for two days and nights and buried the road under enormous drifts. Then, no sooner had they made the road passable and a couple of lorries gone by, than it got suddenly warmer. Within a day everything was thawing out, damp mist hung in the air and rivulets gurgled as they burrowed into the snow, and you could get stuck up to the top of your knee-boots.

Two weeks passed before the tractor could get at the dismantled top room. All this time Matryona went around like someone lost. What particularly upset her was that her three sisters came and with one voice called her a fool for giving the top room away, said they didn't want to see her any more, and went off. At about the same time the lame cat strayed and was seen no more. It was just one thing after another. This was another blow to Matryona.

At last the frost got a grip on the slushy road. A sunny day came along and everybody felt more cheerful. Matryona had had a lucky dream the night before. In the morning she heard that I wanted to take a photograph of somebody at an old-fashioned hand-loom. (There were looms still standing in two cottages in the village; they wove coarse rugs on them.) She smiled shyly and said, 'You just wait a day or two, Ignatich, I'll just send the top room there off and I'll put my loom up, I've still got it, you know, and then you can snap me. Honest to God!'

She was obviously attracted by the idea of posing in an old-fashioned setting. The red, frosty sun tinged the window of the curtailed passageway with a faint pink, and this reflected light warmed Matryona's face. People who are at ease with their consciences always have nice faces.

Coming back from school before dusk I saw some movement near our house. A big new tractor-drawn sledge was already fully loaded, and there was no room for a lot of the timbers, so old Faddei's family and the helpers they had called in had nearly finished knocking together another home-made sledge. They were all working like madmen, in the frenzy that comes upon people when there is a smell of good money in the air or when they are looking forward to some treat. They were shouting at one another and arguing.

They could not agree whether the sledges should be hauled separately or both together. One of Faddei's sons (the lame one) and the engine-driver son-in-law reasoned that the sledges couldn't both be taken at once because the tractor wouldn't be able to pull them. The man in charge of the tractor, a hefty fat-faced fellow who was very sure of himself, said hoarsely that he knew best, he was the driver, and he would take both at once. His motives were obvious: according to the agreement the engine-driver was paying him for the removal of the upper room not for the number of trips he had to make. He could never have made two trips in a night—twenty-five kilometres each way, and one return journey. And by morning he had to get the tractor back in the garage from which he had sneaked it out for this job on the side.

Old Faddei was impatient to get the top room moved that day, and at a nod from him his lads gave in. To the stout sledge in front they hitched the one which they had knocked together in such a hurry.

Matryona was running about amongst the men, fussing and helping them to heave the beams on to the sledge. Suddenly I noticed that she was wearing my jerkin and had dirtied the sleeves on the frozen mud round the beams. I was annoyed, and told her so. That jerkin held memories for me: it had kept me warm in the bad years.

This was the first time that I was ever angry with Matryona Vasilyevna.

Matryona was taken aback. 'Oh dear, dear me,' she said. 'My poor head. I picked it up in a rush, you see, and never thought about it being yours. I'm sorry, Ignatich.'

And she took it off and hung it up to dry.

The loading was finished, and all the men who had been working, about ten of them, clattered past my table and dived under the curtain into the kitchen. I could hear the muffled rattle of glasses and, from time to time, the clink of a bottle, the voices got louder and louder, the boasting more reckless. The biggest braggart was the tractor-driver. The stench of hooch floated in to me. But they didn't go on drinking long. It was getting dark and they had to hurry. They began to leave. The tractor-driver came out first, looking pleased with himself and fierce. The engine-driver son-in-law, Faddei's lame son and one of his nephews were going to Cherusti. The others went off home. Faddei was flourishing his stick, trying to overtake somebody and put him right about something. The lame son paused at my table

78

to light up and suddenly started telling me how he loved Aunt Matryona, and that he had got married not long ago, and his wife had just had a son. Then they shouted for him and he went out. The tractor set up a roar outside.

After all the others had gone Matryona dashed out from behind the screen. She looked after them, anxiously shaking her head. She had put on her jerkin and her head-scarf. As she was going through the door she said to me, 'Why ever couldn't they hire two? If one tractor had cracked up the other would have pulled them. What'll happen now, God only knows!'

She ran out after the others.

After the booze-up and the arguments and all the coming and going it was quieter than ever in the deserted cottage, and very chilly because the door had been opened so many times. I got into my jerkin and sat down to mark exercise books. The noise of the tractor died away in the distance.

An hour went by. And another. And a third. Matryona still hadn't come back, but I wasn't surprised. When she had seen the sledge off she must have gone round to her friend Masha.

Another hour went by. And yet another. Darkness and with it a deep silence had descended on the village. I couldn't understand at the time why it was so quiet. Later I found out that it was because all evening not a single train had gone along the line five hundred yards from the house. No sound was coming from my radio and I noticed that the mice were wilder than ever. Their scampering and scratching and squeaking behind the wallpaper was getting noisier and more defiant all the time.

I woke up. It was 1 o'clock in the morning and Matryona still hadn't come home.

Suddenly I heard several people talking loudly. They were still a long way off, but something told me that they were coming to our house. And sure enough I heard soon afterwards a heavy knock at the gate. A commanding voice, strange to me, yelled out an order to open up. I went out into the pitch darkness with a torch. The whole village was asleep, there was no light in the windows, and the snow had started melting in the last week so that it gave no reflected light. I turned the catch and let them in. Four men in greatcoats went on towards the house. It's a very unpleasant thing to be visited at night by noisy people in greatcoats.

When we got into the light though, I saw that two of them were wearing railway uniforms. The older of the two, a fat man with the same sort of face as the tractor-driver, asked, 'Where's the woman of the house?'

'I don't know.'

'This is the place the tractor with a sledge came from?'

'This is it.'

'Had they been drinking before they left?'

All four of them were looking around them, screwing up their eyes in the dim light from the table-lamp. I realized that they had either made an arrest or wanted to make one.

'What's happened then?'

'Answer the question!'

'But . . .'

'Were they drunk when they went?'

'Were they drinking here?'

Had there been a murder? Or hadn't they been able to move the top room? The men in greatcoats had me off balance. But one thing was certain: Matryona could do time for making hooch.

I stepped back to stand between them and the kitchen door. 'I honestly didn't notice. I didn't see anything.' (I really hadn't seen anything—only heard.) I made what was supposed to be a helpless gesture, drawing attention to the state of the cottage: a table-lamp shining peacefully on books and exercises, a crowd of frightened rubber plants, the austere couch of a recluse, not a sign of debauchery.

They had already seen for themselves, to their annoyance, that there had been no drinking in that room. They turned to leave, telling each other this wasn't where the drinking had been then, but it would be a good thing to put in that it was. I saw them out and tried to discover what had happened. It was only at the gate that one of them growled. 'They've all been cut to bits. Can't find all the pieces.'

'That's a detail. The 9 o'clock express nearly went off the rails. That would have been something.' And they walked briskly away.

I went back to the hut in a daze. Who were 'they'? What did 'all of them' mean? And where was Matryona?

I moved the curtain aside and went into the kitchen. The stink of hooch rose and hit me. It was a deserted battlefield: a huddle of stools and benches, empty bottles lying around, one bottle half-full, glasses, the remains of pickled herring, onion, and sliced fat pork.

Everything was deathly still. Just cockroaches creeping unperturbed about the field of battle.

They had said something about the 9 o'clock express. Why? Perhaps I should have shown them all this? I began to wonder whether I had done right. But what a damnable way to behave—keeping their explanations for official persons only.

Suddenly the small gate creaked. I hurried out on to the landing. 'Matryona Vasilyevna?'

The yard door opened, and Matryona's friend Masha came in, swaying and wringing her hands. 'Matryona . . . our Matryona, Ignatich . . .'

I sat her down and through her tears she told me the story.

The approach to the crossing was a steep rise. There was no barrier. The tractor and the first sledge went over, but the tow-rope broke and the second sledge, the home-made one, got stuck on the crossing and started falling apart—the wood Faddei had given them to make the second sledge was no good. They towed the first sledge out of the way and went back for the second. They were fixing the tow-rope—the tractor-driver and Faddei's lame son, and Matryona, heaven knows what brought her there, was with them, between the tractor and the sledge. What help did she think she could be to the men? She was for ever meddling in men's work. Hadn't a bolting horse nearly tipped her into the lake once, through a hole in the ice?

Why did she have to go to the damned crossing? She had handed over the top room, and owed nothing to anybody . . .

The engine-driver kept a look-out in case the train from Cherusti rushed up on them. Its headlamps would be visible a long way off. But two engines coupled together came from the other direction, from our station, backing without lights. Why they were without lights nobody knows. When an engine is backing, coal-dust blows into the driver's eyes from the tender and he can't see very well. The two engines flew into them and crushed the three people between the tractor and the sledge to pulp. The tractor was wrecked, the sledge was matchwood, the rails were buckled, and both engines turned over.

'But how was it they didn't hear the engines coming?'

'The tractor engine was making such a din.'

'What about the bodies?'

'They won't let anybody in. They've roped them off.'

'What was that somebody was telling me about the express?'

The 9 o'clock express goes through our station at a good speed and on to the crossing. But the two drivers weren't hurt when their engines crashed, they jumped out and ran back along the line waving their hands and they managed to stop the train . . . The nephew was hurt by a beam as well. He's hiding at Klavka's now so that they won't know he was at the crossing. If they find out they'll drag him in as a witness . . . 'Don't know lies up, and do know gets tied up. Kira's husband didn't get a scratch. He tried to hang himself, they had to cut him down. It's all because of me, he says, my aunty's killed and my brother. Now he's gone and given himself up. But the mad-house is where he'll be going, not prison. Oh, Matryona, my dearest Matryona . . .'

Matryona was gone. Someone close to me had been killed. And on her last day I had scolded her for wearing my jerkin.

The lovingly-drawn red and yellow woman in the book advertisement smiled happily on.

Old Masha sat there weeping a little longer. Then she got up to go. And suddenly she asked me, 'Ignatich, you remember, Matryona had a grey shawl. She meant it to go to my Tanya when she died, didn't she?'

She looked at me hopefully in the half-darkness . . . surely I hadn't forgotten?

No, I remembered. 'She said so, yes.'

'Well, listen, maybe you could let me take it with me now. The family will be swarming in tomorrow and I'll never get it then.' And she gave me another hopeful, imploring look. She had been Matryona's friend for half a century, the only one in the village who truly loved her.

No doubt she was right.

'Of course . . . take it.'

She opened the chest, took out the shawl, tucked it under her coat and went out.

The mice had gone mad. They were running furiously up and down the walls, and you could almost see the green wallpaper rippling and rolling over their backs.

In the morning I had to go to school. The time was 3 o'clock. The only thing to do was to lock up and go to bed.

Lock up, because Matryona would not be coming.

I lay down, leaving the light on. The mice were squeaking, almost moaning, racing and running. My mind was weary and wandering, and I couldn't rid myself of an uneasy feeling that an invisible Matryona was flitting about and saying good-bye to her home.

And suddenly I imagined Faddei standing there, young and black-haired, in the dark patch by the door, with his axe uplifted. 'If it wasn't my own brother I'd chop the both of you to bits.'

The threat had lain around for forty years, like an old broad-sword in a corner, and in the end it had struck its blow.

When it was light the women went to the crossing and brought back all that was left of Matryona on a hand-sledge with a dirty sack over it. They threw off the sack to wash her. There was just a mess . . . no feet, only half a body, no left hand. One woman said, 'The Lord has left her her right hand. She'll be able to say her prayers where she's going . . .'

Then the whole crowd of rubber plants was carried out

of the cottage . . . these plants that Matryona had loved so much that once when smoke woke her up in the night she didn't rush to save her house but to tip the plants on to the floor in case they were suffocated. The women swept the floor clean. They hung a wide towel of old home-spun over Matryona's dim mirror. They took down the jolly posters. They moved my table out of the way. Under the icons, near the windows, they stood a rough unadorned coffin on a row of stools.

In the coffin lay Matryona. Her body, mangled and lifeless, was covered with a clean sheet. Her head was swathed in a white kerchief. Her face was almost undamaged, peaceful, more alive than dead.

The villagers came to pay their last respects. The women even brought their small children to take a look at the dead. And if anyone raised a lament, all the women, even those who had looked in out of idle curiosity, always joined in, wailing where they stood by the door or the wall, as though they were providing a choral accompaniment. The men stood stiff and silent with their caps off.

The formal lamentation had to be performed by the women of Matryona's family. I observed that the lament followed a coldly calculated age-old ritual. The more distant relatives went up to the coffin for a short while and made low wailing noises over it. Those who considered themselves closer kin to the dead woman began their lament in the doorway and when they got as far as the coffin, bowed down and roared out their grief right in the face of the departed. Every lamenter made up her own melody. And expressed her own thoughts and feelings.

I realized that a lament for the dead is not just a lament, but a kind of politics. Matryona's three sisters swooped, took possession of the cottage, the goat, and the stove, locked up the chest, ripped the 200 roubles for the funeral out of the coat lining, and drummed it into everybody who came that only they were near relatives. Their lament over the coffin went like this, '*Oh, nanny, nanny! Oh nan-nan!* All we had in the world was you! You could have lived in peace and quiet, you could. And we should always have been kind and loving to you. Now your top room's been the death of you. Finished you off it has, the cursed thing! Oh why did you have to take it down? Why didn't you listen to us?'

Thus the sisters' laments were indictments of Matryona's husband's family: they shouldn't have made her take the top room down. (There was an underlying meaning too: you've taken the top room all right but we won't let you have the house itself!)

Matryona's husband's family, her sisters-in-law, Yefim and Faddei's sisters, and various nieces lamented like this, '*Oh poor auntie, poor auntie!* Why didn't you take better care of yourself! Now they're angry with us for sure. Our own dear Matryona you were, and it's your own fault! The top room is nothing to do with it. Oh why did you go where death was waiting for you? Nobody asked you to go there. And what a way to die! Oh why didn't you listen to us?' (Their answer to the others showed through these laments: we are not to blame for her death, and the house we'll talk about later.)

But the 'second' Matryona, a coarse, broad-faced woman, the substitute Matryona whom Faddei had married so long ago for the sake of her name, got out of step with family policy, wailing and sobbing over the coffin in her simplicity, '*Oh my poor dear sister!* You won't be angry with me, will you now? Oh-oh-oh! How we used to talk and talk, you and me! Forgive a poor miserable woman! You've gone to be with your dear mother, and you'll come for me some day for sure! Oh-oh-oh-oh! . . .'

At every 'oh-oh-oh' it was as though she were giving up the ghost. She writhed and gasped, with her breast against the side of the coffin. When her lament went beyond the ritual prescription the women, as though acknowledging its success, all started saying, 'Come away now, come away.'

Matryona came away, but back she went again, sobbing with even greater abandon. Then an ancient woman came out of a corner, put her hand on Matryona's shoulder, and said, 'There are two riddles in this world: how I was born I don't remember, how I shall die I don't know.'

And Matryona fell silent at once, and all the others were silent, so that there was an unbroken hush.

But the old woman herself, who was much older than all the other old women there and didn't seem to belong to Matryona at all, after a while started wailing, 'Oh, my poor sick Matryona! Oh my poor Vasilyevna! Oh what a weary thing it is to be seeing you into your grave!'

There was one who didn't follow the ritual, but wept straightforwardly, in the fashion of our age, which has had plenty of practice at it. This was Matryona's unfortunate foster-daughter, Kira, from Cherusti, for whom the top room had been taken down and moved. Her ringlets were pitifully out of curl. Her eyes looked red and bloodshot. She didn't notice that her headscarf was slipping off out in the frosty air and that her arm hadn't found the sleeve of her coat. She walked in a stupor from her foster-mother's coffin in one house to her brother's in another. They were afraid she would lose her mind, because her husband had to go for trial as well.

It looked as if her husband was doubly at fault: not only had he been moving the top room, but as an engine-driver he knew the regulations about unprotected crossings, and should have gone down to the station to warn them about the tractor. There were a thousand people on the Urals express that night, peacefully sleeping in the upper and lower berths of their dimly-lit carriages, and all those lives were nearly cut short. All because of a few greedy people, wanting to get their hands on a plot of land, or not wanting to make a second trip with a tractor.

All because of the top room, which had been under a curse ever since Faddei's hands had started itching to take it down.

The tractor-driver was already beyond human justice. And the railway authorities were also at fault, both because a busy crossing was unguarded and because the coupled engines were travelling without lights. That was why they had tried at first to blame it all on the drink, and then to keep the case out of court.

The rails and the track were so twisted and torn that for three days, while the coffins were still in the house, no trains ran—they were diverted on to another line. All Friday, Saturday, and Sunday, from the end of the investigation until the funeral, the work of repairing the line went on day and night. The repair gang was frozen, and they made fires to warm themselves and to light their work at night, using the boards and beams from the second sledge which were there for the taking, scattered around the crossing.

The first sledge just stood there, undamaged and still loaded, a little way beyond the crossing.

One sledge, tantalizingly ready to be towed away, and the other perhaps still to be plucked from the flames—that was what harrowed the soul of black-bearded Faddei all day Friday and all day Saturday. His daughter was going out of her mind, his son-in-law had a criminal charge hanging over him, in his own house lay the son he had killed, and along the street the woman he had killed and whom he had once loved. But Faddei stood by the coffins clutching his beard only for a short time, and went away again. His tall brow was clouded by painful thoughts, but what he was thinking about was how to save the timbers of the top room from the flames and from Matryona's scheming sisters.

Going over the people of Talnovo in my mind I realized that Faddei was not the only one like that.

Property, the people's property, or my property, is strangely called our 'goods'. If you lose your goods, people think you disgrace yourself and make yourself look foolish.

Faddei dashed about, never stopping to sit down, from the settlement to the station, from one official to another, stood there with his bent back, leaning heavily on his stick, and begged them all to take pity on an old man and give him permission to recover the top room.

Somebody gave permission. And Faddei gathered together his surviving sons, sons-in-law and nephews, got horses from the kolkhoz and from the other side of the wrecked crossing, by a roundabout way that led through three villages, brought the remnants of the top room home to his yard. He finished the job in the early hours of Sunday morning.

On Sunday afternoon they were buried. The two coffins met in the middle of the village, and the relatives argued

87

about which of them should go first. Then they put them side by side on an open sledge, the aunt and the nephew, and carried the dead over the damp snow, with a gloomy February sky above, to the churchyard two villages away. There was an unkind wind, so the priest and the deacon waited inside the church and didn't come out to Talnovo to meet them.

A crowd of people walked slowly behind the coffins, singing in chorus. Outside the village they fell back.

When Sunday came the women were still fussing around the house. An old woman mumbled psalms by the coffin, Matryona's sisters flitted about, popping things into the oven, and the air round the mouth of the stove trembled with the heat of red-hot peats, those which Matryona had carried in a sack from a distant bog. They were making unappetizing pies with poor flour.

When the funeral was over and it was already getting on towards evening, they gathered for the wake. Tables were put together to make a long one, which hid the place where the coffin had stood in the morning. To start with they all stood round the table, and an old man, the husband of a sister-in-law, said the Lord's Prayer. Then they poured everybody a little honey and warm water, just enough to cover the bottom of the bowl. We spooned it up without bread or anything, in memory of the dead. Then we ate something and drank vodka and the conversation became more animated. Before the jelly they all stood up and sang 'Eternal remembrance' (they explained to me that it had to be sung before the jelly). There was more drinking. By now they were talking louder than ever, and not about Matryona at all. The sister-in-law's husband started boasting, 'Did you notice, brother Christians, that they took the funeral service slowly today? That's because Father Mikhail noticed me. He knows I know the service. Other times it's saints defend us, homeward wend us, and that's all.'

At last the supper was over. They all rose again. They sang 'Worthy is she'. Then again, with a triple repetition of 'Eternal remembrance'. But the voices were hoarse and out of tune, their faces drunken, and nobody put any feeling into this 'eternal memory'.

Then the main guests went away, and only the near relatives were left. They pulled out their cigarettes and lit up, there were jokes and laughter. There was some mention of Matryona's husband and his disappearance. The sister-in-law's husband, striking himself on the chest, assured me and the cobbler who was married to one of Matryona's sisters, 'He was dead, Yefim was dead! What could stop him coming back if he wasn't? If I knew they were going to hang me when I got to the old country I'd come back just the same!'

The cobbler nodded in agreement. He was a deserter and had never left the old country. All through the war he was hiding in his mother's cellar.

The stern and silent old woman who was more ancient than all the ancients was staying the night and sat high up on the stove. She looked down in mute disapproval on the indecently animated youngsters of fifty and sixty.

But the unhappy foster-daughter, who had grown up within these walls, went away behind the kitchen screen to cry.

Faddei didn't come to Matryona's wake—perhaps because he was holding a wake for his son. But twice in the next few days he walked angrily into the house for discussions with Matryona's sisters and the deserting cobbler.

The argument was about the house. Should it go to one of the sisters or to the foster-daughter? They were on the verge of taking it to court, but they made peace because they realized that the court would hand over the house to neither side, but to the Rural District Council. A bargain was struck. One sister took the goat, the cobbler and his wife got the house, and to make up Faddei's share, since he had 'nursed every bit of timber here in his arms', in addition to the top room which had already been carried away, they let him have the shed which had housed the goat, and the whole of the inner fence between the yard and the garden.

Once again the insatiable old man got the better of sickness and pain and became young and active. Once again he gathered together his surviving sons and sons-in-law, and they dismantled the shed and the fence, and he hauled the timbers himself, sledge by sledge, and only towards the end did he have Antoshka of 8-D, who didn't slack this time, to help him.

They boarded Matryona's house up till the spring, and I moved in with one of her sisters-in-law, not far away. This sister-in-law on several occasions came out with some recollection of Matryona, and made me see the dead woman in a new light. 'Yefim didn't love her. He used to say, 'I like to dress in an educated way, but she dresses any old way, like they do in the country.' Well then, he thinks, if she doesn't want anything, he might as well drink whatever's to spare. One time I went with him to the town to work, and he got himself a madam there and never wanted to come back to Matryona.'

Everything she said about Matryona was disapproving. She was slovenly, she made no effort to get a few things about her. She wasn't the saving kind. She didn't even keep a pig, because she didn't like fattening them up for some reason. And the silly woman helped other people without payment. (What brought Matryona to mind this time was that the garden needed ploughing and she couldn't find enough helpers to pull the plough.)

Matryona's sister-in-law admitted that she was warm-hearted and straightforward, but pitied and despised her for it.

It was only then, after these disapproving comments from her sister-in-law, that a true likeness of Matryona formed itself before my eyes, and I understood her as I never had when I lived side by side with her.

Of course! Every house in the village kept a pig. But she didn't. What can be easier than fattening a greedy piglet that cares for nothing in the world but food! You warm his swill three times a day, you live for him—then you cut his throat and you have some fat.

But she had none . . .

She made no effort to get things round her . . . She didn't

struggle and strain to buy things and then care for them more than life itself.

She didn't go all out after fine clothes. Clothes, that beautify what is ugly and evil.

She was misunderstood and abandoned even by her husband. She had lost six children, but not her sociable ways. She was a stranger to her sisters and sisters-in-law, a ridiculous creature who stupidly worked for others without pay. She didn't accumulate property against the day she died. A dirty-white goat, a gammy-legged cat, some rubber plants . . .

We had all lived side by side with her and never understood that she was that righteous one without whom, as the proverb says, no village can stand.

Nor any city.

Nor our whole land.

translated by H. T. Willetts

Adam and Eve

YURI KAZAKOV

THE PAINTER Ageyev was staying at a hotel in a northern town where he had come to paint the fishermen. The town was spaciously laid out; it had broad squares, streets, and avenues, and because of this it looked empty.

It was autumn. Low, ragged clouds came scudding from the west over the grey-brown woods misted with hoar-frost, it rained a dozen times a day, and the lake loomed over the town like a leaden wall. Ageyev stayed late in bed, smoked on an empty stomach, and stared at the window lined and streaming with rain. Below it the roofs of the houses gleamed sullenly, reflecting the sky; the room reeked of tobacco smoke and of something else peculiar to hotel rooms. His head ached, he had a ceaseless buzzing in his ears and an occasional twinge of pain in his heart.

Ageyev had been talented from his childhood up, and now, at twenty-five, his expression was scornful: there was a disdain, a weariness about the drooping brown eyelids and the lower lip, and his dark eyes were languid and arrogant. He wore a velvet jacket and a beret, and walked with a slouch, his hands in his pockets, hardly seeming to give an inattentive glance to people in the street or indeed to anything he came across in general, but retaining of everything a memory so indestructibly sharp that his breast actually ached with it.

There was nothing for him to do in the town itself and he spent the morning sitting at the table in his room holding his head, or lying down, waiting for 12 o'clock when the bar would open downstairs. When at last it came he walked down unsteadily, and each time looked with hatred at the picture in the hall. The picture showed the near-by lake with its inlets, and an unnaturally orange growth of stunted birches on the ledges of unnaturally purple rocks. It was autumn in the picture as well.

In the bar he ordered a brandy and squinting inwards with the effort of not spilling it slowly drank it down. Having drunk, he lit a cigarette, and looked round at whoever might be there as he waited impatiently for the first jolting warmth which he knew would at once make him feel well, and lovingly disposed to everything—life, people, the town, and even the rain.

After that he would go out and walk about the streets, wondering where to go with Vika, and what to do in general and how to go on living. A couple of hours later he was back in the hotel; by then he was sleepy and he went to bed and slept.

And when he woke up he went down again, to the restaurant. Now the day was nearly over, it was dusk outside the windows, and when evening came the jazz band in the restaurant struck up. Girls with made-up faces came in, sat in pairs at little tables, chewed wax-like chops, drank vermouth, danced with anyone who asked them, and wore an expression of happiness and of intoxication with high life. Ageyev gazed in misery round the large, familiar, smoke-filled hall. He hated the girls, and their boyfriends, and the wretched band with its piercing pipes and thumping drums, and the awful food, and the local vodka which the waitress invariably served short.

At midnight the restaurant closed. Ageyev staggered back to his third floor, wheezed as he fumbled at the keyhole, undressed, made mooing noises, ground his teeth, and pitched headlong into blackness until morning.

That day was like all the others, but on the next at 2 o'clock he went to meet Vika's train. He arrived early and, with only a brief glance at the platform and the passengers with their luggage, went straight into the refreshment room. Yet there had been a time when the mere sight of a railway platform excited him and filled him with wanderlust.

93

A tall waitress with red hair brought him his vodka.

'What a girl,' Ageyev muttered, his eyes following her with greedy pleasure, and when she came up to him again he said: 'Hello, baby. You're just what I've been looking for all my life.'

The waitress smiled unmoved. She was used to hearing this sort of thing from almost everyone. People would drop in for half an hour and sit muttering—usually vulgarities—never to come back and see the station or the red-haired waitress again.

'I must paint you,' said Ageyev, getting tipsy. 'I'm an artist.'

She shifted the glasses on his table and smiled: she liked hearing it all the same.

'You listen to me, I'm a genius, I'm known in the West! What about it?'

'It is not us the artists come to paint.' She spoke with a slightly un-Russian accent.

'How do you know?' He looked at her breast.

'Oh! They always want fishermen. And workmen—signalmen. Or else there's a little island with a wooden church —they all go there, they come . . . from Moscow, from Leningrad. And they're all like you—with berets—that what you call them?'

'They're all idiots. Well, we'll meet again, eh?' he added hurriedly as he heard the sound of the approaching train. 'What's your name?'

'Zhanna, if you must know.'

'You're not Russian, are you?'

'No, I'm a Finn. Yuonaleinen.'

'Hell of a name,' Ageyev mumbled, finishing his vodka and coughing.

He paid, gave Zhanna's shoulder a squeeze, and walked out on to the platform in high spirits. 'What a waste of a woman!' he thought, screwing up his eyes at the light-blue express as its coaches flashed past him. The eyestrain made him feel giddy and he turned away. 'Shouldn't have had that drink,' he thought absentmindedly and, in a sudden fright at the thought of Vika's arrival, lit a cigarette.

The passengers were already moving from the train to

the exit. He sighed, threw the cigarette away, and went to
look for Vika. She saw him first and shouted to him. He
turned and watched her as she came towards him in her
fleecy black coat. The coat swung unfastened and her knees
pushing at the hem of her skirt made it billow out.

She shyly gave him her net-gloved hand. Her hair,
bleached by the sun, short and ruffled, fell over her forehead. From under it her slanted Tartar eyes looked up at
him alarmed, while her mouth was crimson and taut, with
dry cracked lips half open like a child's.

'Hello,' she said a little breathlessly, and wanted to go on,
perhaps to say something gay and clever, prepared in advance, but faltered into silence.

Ageyev unaccountably fixed his eyes on the transparent
scarf round her neck, then with a scared schoolboy expression snatched her shiny suitcase from her, and together they
walked down the wide street from the station.

'Your face is a bit puffy somehow . . .' she said. 'How
are you getting on?' She looked around her. 'I like it here.'

'Ugh!' He made the unpleasant guttural sound he always
used to express contempt.

'Have you been drinking?' She pushed her hands into her
pockets and bent her head. Her hair fell forward.

'Ugh!' he said again, with a side-glance at Vika.

Vika was very pretty and about her clothes, her ruffled
hair, her way of speaking, there was something elusively
Muscovite to which he had become unused in the north. In
Moscow they had only met a couple of times, they didn't
know each other properly, and her arrival, the leave he
knew she had wangled with difficulty, and the fact—which
he also sensed—that she was ready for anything, all struck
him as somehow unexpected and strange.

'I'm lucky with women,' he thought with pleased surprise,
and deliberately stopped as if to put on his gloves, but really
to look at Vika from the back. She slowed down, half-turning
and looking at him questioningly, then glanced round absentmindedly at the shops and the passers-by.

She was pretty from the back as well, and the fact that
she had not walked on but slowed down with that interro-
gative glance which seemed in itself to express her depend-

ence on him—all this pleased him enormously, even though a moment ago he had felt embarrassed and confused by her arrival. He vaguely realized that he had only had that drink to get rid of his embarrassment.

'I've brought you your press cuttings,' said Vika when he had caught up with her. 'You know they're giving you hell? There was a terrific row going on at the exhibition the day I went.'

'Ugh!' he said again, though with profound satisfaction, adding in immediate alarm: 'They haven't taken down the "Kolkhoz Girl"?'

'No, it's still up,' Vika laughed. 'Nobody can make head or tail of it, they're all shouting and arguing—the boys with the beards and the jeans, they don't know where they are, they're going round in circles.'

'And you, do you like it?'

Vika smiled vaguely, and Ageyev, suddenly furious, frowned and snorted, pouting his lower lip, his dark eyes listless and sullen. 'I'll get drunk,' he decided.

And all that day he walked about the town with Vika like a stranger, yawned, mumbled indistinguishable answers to her questions, waited at the pier while she found out the times of the steamers, and in the evening got drunk, hard as she begged him not to, locked himself in his room, and, while knowing with deep, acute pain that she was alone in hers, upset and bewildered, only smoked and sniggered to himself. And thought about red-haired Zhanna.

The telephone rang a couple of times. He knew it was Vika, but let it ring. 'Go chase yourself, you silly goose,' he thought furiously.

The next day Vika woke Ageyev early and made him wash and dress while she packed his rucksack herself, dragged his paintbox, easel, and fishing tackle from under the bed, looked in the desk drawers, clinked empty bottles, and was generally aloof and businesslike, paying him no attention whatever.

'Just like a wife,' thought Ageyev, watching her in amazement. He scowled and thought how quickly a woman could get used to a man and become as cold and masterful as if they had been living together for ages.

He had a headache and wanted to go down to the bar but, remembering it wouldn't yet be open, coughed, grunted, lit a cigarette on an empty stomach, and felt still worse. Meanwhile Vika had been down and paid the bill and called a taxi. 'Oh hell, let her,' he thought dully, going out and getting into it. He sat back and closed his eyes. The early morning rain meant that it would rain all day. It even began to snow, the heavy, wet flakes falling fast and turning black almost before the first touch of the wet roofs and pavements.

At the pier Ageyev felt worse than ever. Overcome with misery, half asleep and without an idea of why or where he was going, he listened drowsily to the wind hooting and whistling, water smacking the landing steps, motor-boats starting up on a high note, spluttering and dying down. Vika too had quite lost her spirits and was sad and cold as she sat beside him looking round helplessly, wilting in her short tight trousers and still bareheaded. The wind ruffled her hair and blew it over her forehead, and she looked as if she had just received a telegram and was going to a funeral.

'She would wear trousers,' Ageyev thought spitefully, closing his eyes and trying to make himself comfortable against the wooden partition. 'Where the devil am I off to? God, I feel awful!'

They could hardly wait for their boat and watched impatiently as it pulled alongside, hissing, steaming, pounding, creaking against the pier and scraping white shavings off its timber stanchions.

Even when they went aboard Ageyev felt no better. Somewhere down below, where everything blissfully seethed and rumbled, and yellow pistons went up and down in hot oil, it was warm, but the forward cabin was gloomy, cold, and had a musty smell. The wind howled, the waves splashed against the sides of the ship, and glasses tinkled nervously as it gently lurched. Brown, thinned-out woods, villages darkened by the rain, buoys and battered markers drifted slowly past the bleary portholes. Ageyev shivered feverishly and went out.

D

After wandering about on the ribbed metal flooring of the lower deck, he found shelter next to the engine room and close to the restaurant. The restaurant was not yet open, although an evil smell came from the salt cod cooking in the galley. Ageyev climbed on to the warm top of a metal bunker, leaned against a stack of birch logs glossy in their satin bark, and listened to the measured sighing of the engine, the splashing of the paddles and the discordant voices of the passengers. As usual those who were still excited by their send-off were gabbling noisily and cracking jokes, while from the stern came the sounds of a concertina, shouts, and the loud tapping of heels on the iron deck.

Near the hot water tap tea was being brewed in mugs and teapots, and people sat on bundles and suitcases, drinking it and breaking pieces off French rolls, glancing out, warm and cosy, at the dark dishevelled waves which the wind chased across the lake. Women were taking off their kerchiefs and doing their hair, children had already settled down to play and were running and bustling about.

The lights went on, yellow through frosted glass, and at once it became still more dark and cold outside. Ageyev idly shifted his gaze. The gangways were cluttered up with sacks of potatoes, hampers, barrels of gherkins and bales of other stuff. The passengers were all people from the neighbourhood, making their way to some place or other up the coast, and their talk was all of local things: cattle, new regulations, mothers-in-law, fishing, the lumber camps, and the weather.

'It doesn't matter!' thought Ageyev. 'It's only one day— then the island, a cottage, silence and solitude . . . It doesn't matter!'

The restaurant opened at last, and immediately Vika pushed her way towards him through the crowd. She gave him a sad look and a smile.

'Want a drink, you poor dear?' she said. 'Well go along and get it!'

Ageyev went and came back with a small bottle and some bread and gherkins. Vika, who had climbed on to the bunker, met him with a look of attentive concern. He sat down next to her, worked the cork out of the bottle, took a pull at it and munched a gherkin. Feeling better, he turned to her with a certain animation.

'Eat!' he mumbled, and Vika too began to eat.

'Tell me, what's the matter with you?' she asked after a while.

Ageyev had another drink and thought a while. Then he lit a cigarette and looked down at the suede shoe dangling from Vika's foot.

'Just fed up, old girl,' he said quietly. 'I expect I'm just no good as an artist and a fool as well. Here I am painting on and on with everybody telling me it's no good, it's all wrong . . .

What do they say? "Ideological immaturity!" "On a slippery slope!" "A spirit alien to our people!" . . . As if the whole nation were behind them nodding in agreement. You know?'

'You're silly!' Vika said gently. She suddenly laughed and put her head on his shoulder. Her hair had a strange, bitter smell. Ageyev rubbed his cheek against it and shut his eyes.

Suddenly she was close and dear to him. He remembered the first time he kissed her in Moscow, in the passage at the flat of an artist friend. He had arrived a little drunk and gay, Vika was quiet and looked bewildered; they had had a long talk in the kitchen, or rather he had talked to her, telling her he was a genius and no one else was any good. Then they went to join the others and in the passage he kissed her and told her he was terribly in love with her.

She didn't believe him but she caught her breath and blushed, her eyes dark and her lips dry, and began to chatter and laugh with some other girls who were there without looking at him again. He too stuck to the men, arguing about some drawings or other, and he and Vika sat in different rooms.

Vika talked and giggled with her girl-friends and with someone who kept coming in and going out, feeling happy because he was in the next room sitting in an arm-chair and, like her, making conversation with someone. She told him so afterwards.

It was good now, in this out-of-the-way place in the north, suddenly to remember that recent yet for ever vanished evening. It meant that they had a past. They did not yet really love each other, nothing bound them together, they were still seeing other people who had been in their lives before, they had never spent a night together, they still didn't know one another. But they already had a past, and this was good.

'Seriously,' said Ageyev, 'out here I've kept on thinking about my life. You know it was horrid here without you, pouring with rain and nowhere to go. I sat in my room or downstairs, drunk, and kept brooding . . . I've just about had enough. When I was at art school I used to imagine I'd turn everything upside down, I'd knock them all sideways with my painting. I'd travel, I'd live in a cave—like a sort of Rockwell Kent, you know. Then I got my diploma and at once they started on me—'You bastard, you so-and-so!'— preaching at me. They haven't stopped hounding me ever since, the swine. And the longer it goes on the worse it gets. "You abstractionist, you neo-realist, you formalist, you've got this and that deviation—just you wait, we'll get you!" . . .'

He moved a little aside from her and had another drink. His headache had stopped, and he felt like sitting and talking and thinking on and on, because Vika was sitting next to him and listening. He looked at her out of the corner of his eyes—her face was alive and grave, the eyes under their shadow of lashes long and black. He looked closer—they really were black, and her lips were rough, and Ageyev's heart began to thump. As for Vika, she had tucked up her feet on the bunker, unfastened her coat, propped her chin on her knees and was gazing into his face.

'You're not looking well,' she said, touching his chin. 'You haven't shaved, you're so rough.'

'I'm kind of stale, he grinned and looked away at the lake. 'I keep on thinking about myself and Van Gogh . . . Do I really have to kick the bucket too before they take me seriously? As if my colours, my drawing, my figures weren't as good as theirs. All those opportunists—I'm sick of the whole business!'

'You don't expect time-servers to admit you're any good,' she said quickly, as though by the way.

'Why not?'

'I just know . . . For them to recognize you they'd have to recognize they've been wrong all their lives.'

'Oh!' Ageyev lit a cigarette and smoked it in silence, looking at his feet and rubbing his face; the stubble on his shallow cheeks scraped against his fingers. 'Three years!' he said. 'And I'm still doing illustrations to earn my keep. Three years since I finished art school, and there are good-for-nothings who envy me: "Ah, he's famous! Ah, he's known in the West . . ." Idiots. If they only knew. Every picture I do . . . And I still haven't a studio. You paint a spring landscape—it's the wrong spring! It isn't nature, it's biology! they say. What do you think of that? You can't get into a show, the selection committees make your life a misery, and if you do get in with something unimportant it's still worse. And the reviewers! They rave about being modern, but what they understand by it is beneath contempt. And the lies they tell, and if they do say a word of truth it's only for a demagogic end!'

'And has there never been a word of truth said about you?' She broke off a sliver of birch and nibbled it thoughtfully.

'Oh you!' Ageyev went pale. 'You little college girl! You're still on the sidelines, you haven't run foul of them, you've got your books, your dialectical materialism, your field-work . . . If they say "man", it has to be with a capital M. Their enlightened gaze sees nothing but Man as a Whole —the country, whole millennia, the cosmos! One individual is no good to them. They don't think about him. You have to give them millions. They hide behind the millions, and we, those of us who are something, we're beatniks . . . Spiritual teddy boys, that's what we are! We haven't a heroic style!' He laughed unpleasantly. 'We don't portray the masses! There they are, the masses,' Ageyev nodded at the passengers. 'And I love them, and it makes me sick to drool over them in ecstasy. I love them in the flesh—their eyes, their

hands—see? Because it's they who hold up the earth. That's
the whole point. If everyone is good, then society is good as
well, that's what I'm telling you! I think about it day and
night. I'm in a bad way, I've no commissions, no money. To
hell with it, I don't mind. What matters is that I'm right all
the same, and let nobody try to teach me. It's life that teaches
me—and as for being optimistic and believing in the future
and in those masses they go on about—I can give 100 yards
start to any one of those critics.'

He snorted, his nostrils flared, and his eyes clouded.

'It's bad for you to drink . . .' Vika said softly, looking up at
him with pity.

'Wait a second!' Ageyev said hoarsely. 'I've got something
the matter with me . . . asthma or something. Can't breathe
properly.'

His cigarette had gone out, he lit it and inhaled but had
a fit of coughing and threw it down, putting one foot on
the floor to stamp it out. He looked at Vika and made a
face.

'Get out of the way, I'm going to bed!' He blinked
angrily, got off the bunker and went below.

While they were talking the heating had been turned on,
the cabin was warm and the porthole had steamed over. Sitting beside it, Ageyev rubbed the glass with his sleeve; his
left eyelid was twitching. He knew that Vika was now his
salvation. But there was something about her that infuriated
him. She had come to him . . . fresh, pretty, in love—oh hell!
Why, why did he always have to be arguing and proving
something or other? And to her of all people! To Vika,
who had come all that way, her heart turning over and her
knees weak at the thought of their first night together, of him,
of holding him close to her, and he the drunken devil . . .
Oh God! And it would all have been all right, perfect—if
only she had agreed with him at once, if she had said, 'Yes,
you're right!' He would have gone out of his mind with joy,
he would have carried her off to the lake, to a cottage, he
would have sat her by the window and rushed to his canvas.
Her tiny face, her slanted eyes and sun-bleached hair, her

chin propped on her fist . . . He might never paint anything better in his life! Oh God!

He began to take off his clothes, feeling lonely and sorry for himself to the point of tears. 'What the hell,' he thought, 'it doesn't matter! It isn't the first time!' He shuddered at the things he had said to her. He must work, not talk.

When he was undressed he climbed on to the upper bunk and turned to the wall, but even then went on moving his head about restlessly on the shiny pillow-case, unable to settle down.

It was evening by the time the steamer neared the island. A brief sunset, dim and remote, burnt itself out, and dusk was falling as the boat nosed its way through countless reefs. They could now see the church with its many domes; as they drew closer to the island it shifted on the horizon, now right, now left, and at one moment was behind them.

Vika had a stubborn, hurt face. Ageyev whistled between his teeth, glancing indifferently from side to side at the flat islands and the villages, and inspecting with some interest the splendid boats which looked like Viking sailing ships.

When they came right up to the island, they saw a windmill and a beautiful ancient farmhouse with its outbuildings and barns—all empty and without a sign of life, like pieces in a museum. Ageyev grinned.

'Just the right thing for me,' he muttered, looking at Vika with rage. 'Right in the forefront of the seven-year plan as you might say—no?'

Vika said nothing. Her expression was now withdrawn as if she had planned it all in advance and come on her own and found everything as expected.

No one except the two of them landed on the island. And there was no one on the open wooden landing-stage except an old woman with a lantern shining, although it was still daylight.

'Well, here we are, you and I, like Adam and Eve.' Ageyev grinned again, stepping down on the damp planks of the jetty.

Vika again made no reply.

A woman in a wadded coat and boots appeared on the bank, smiling in welcome while she was still far off.

'Only the two of you?' she shouted gaily as she hurried towards them, shifting her eyes from one to the other. When she came up to them she took Vika's suitcase from her and talked to them as if they were long-expected guests.

'Well, thank goodness,' she rattled on in her friendly voice, climbing up the bank. 'I was beginning to think no one else would come this year, the season was over, time to dig in for the winter, and now you've come. I'll take you to our hotel.'

'Hotel?' Ageyev asked in his disagreeable voice.

The woman laughed.

'They all say that, they're all surprised, though it's more than a year since I came. Had my old man with me but he died. Now I'm alone. Certainly there's a hotel! For tourists and artists and people like that. There's a lot of them come in the summer and stay on and paint.'

Thinking of his misery at the hotel, Ageyev sighed and screwed up his face. He had been looking forward to a cottage, a small farmhouse with a smell of cows and a porch and an attic.

But the hotel turned out to be attractive. There was a big stove in the kitchen, and three bedrooms—all empty, and another very odd room with slender pillars down the middle, carved and painted in old-Russian style, supporting the ceiling, and big modern windows reaching to the floor on three sides, as in a glassed-in hall.

In every bedroom there were bare beds showing their webbing and bare bedside tables of rough wood.

Ageyev and Vika chose a room with a stove and a window to the south. Framed water-colours hung on the walls. Ageyev glanced at them and twitched his lip. They were painstaking student sketches of either the church or the windmill.

The landlady kept going in and out carrying sheets, pillows, and pillow-cases, and with them came a good smell of clean linen.

'Well, now you can settle down,' she said, pleased. 'That's nice. I get bored all by myself. It's nice in summer with all those jolly painters, but now there's hardly another soul on the island.'

'How do we manage about food?' asked Vika.

'Oh, you won't starve,' she shouted cheerfully from somewhere down the passage. 'There's a village at the other end of the island, you can get milk and things, or there's a shop on Pog Island, you can go by boat. Are you from Leningrad?'

'No, Moscow,' said Vika.

'Well, that's nice, we always get Leningraders. I've plenty of logs and kindling—they were restoring the church last summer, a lot of stuff was left over. And I've got the keys of the church. When you want to go just tell me and I'll open it up.'

The landlady went away and Vika, happy and tired, flopped on her bed.

'It's too good to be true!' she said. 'It really is! It's brilliant of you, my darling Adam. Do you like baked potatoes?'

Ageyev smirked, twitched his lip and went out. He walked quietly past the graveyard round the church. It had grown dark and, as he walked towards it from the east, the church towered above him with its magnificent silhouette, luminous in the spaces between its onion domes and in the open arches of its belfry. Two birds were calling to each other from different places in measured, monotonous voices, and there was a strong smell of grass and of autumn cold.

'It's the end of the world,' thought Ageyev as he passed the church and came to the lake. He went down to the landing-stage and sat on a bollard, looking at the west. A couple of hundred yards away there was another island, flat and bare except for willow bushes. Beyond it lay still another, and there seemed to be a village: a lone light shone far off through the trees. Soon a motor-boat started up on a high thin note somewhere over there, and went on and on, then suddenly spluttered out.

Ageyev felt lonely, but he sat on smoking, getting used to the silence and the clean smell of the autumn freshness and the water, thinking about himself, about his pictures, thinking that he was a messiah, a great artist, and that here he was, all alone at the end of the world, while various critics who lived in Gorky Street in Moscow were at this moment sitting with girls in restaurants, drinking brandy, eating roast chicken, wiping their greasy lips with their napkins and uttering various fine and lofty words, and that everything they said was a lie, because they weren't thinking about lofty things but only about getting the girls into bed. And in the mornings they would take coffee for their hangover and drops for their heart condition, and write articles about him, and again tell lies, because not one of them believed in what he wrote but only thought of how much he would get for it, and not one of them had ever sat in solitude on a damp pier, looking at a dark, uninhabited island and preparing for creative achievement.

These thoughts were both sad and comforting: there was a bitter sweetness in them. He enjoyed thinking such thoughts and he often did.

At one moment he found himself mentally humming the tune, remembered out of the blue, of the old Countess's solo in *The Queen of Spades*. And this ghostly music—which he heard somewhere deep inside him with all its orchestral accompaniment including the sinister note of the clarinets and the bassoons and the painful suspense of the pauses— began to terrify him because it was death.

Then, as suddenly and sharply, to the point of pain, like the longing for air, he felt a longing for the smell of tea—not brewed tea, not tea in a glass, but dry tea leaves. At once there came to him straight out of his childhood, the memory of a milky glass teapot with a touching landscape painted on it, and his dream of living in the little house with the red roof, and the dry rustling sound as his mother took the lid off the teapot and poured the tea leaves in, and the smell as the cloudy-opal teapot filled with darkness.

This immediately made him remember his mother, her love for him, her life lived in him and for him. And himself, so quick and lively, with moments of such unaccountable joy and vitality that he could hardly believe that this could ever have been himself.

With belated pain he thought of how often he had been rude, inconsiderate, and unfeeling towards his mother, how rarely, while he had the chance, he had been willing to listen to her childhood stories of a remote, long-vanished past. Of how little, in his childish selfishness, he had appreciated the constancy of her love, a love such as he had never since experienced from anyone in all his life.

And remembering all this, he at once began to doubt himself and to think that perhaps his critics were right and he was wrong and was doing nothing as it should be done. He thought that all his life some basic idea—an idea in the highest sense—must have been lacking in him. That he had all too often, talented as he was, looked down with lazy indifference on everything except his talent and his life—and this at such a time!

With helpless rage he remembered all the arguments he had had, ever since his student days, with painters, with art experts, with whoever would not accept his view of painting, colour, design. He thought now that the reason he could not convince them, rout them, prove to them his messianic role, was that he lacked the inspiration of an idea. How indeed could you have a prophet without an idea?

So he sat for a long time. Vika came out of the house, walked a little way along the wooden boards towards the shore, stood looking around her and called him in a low voice. He heard her but neither moved nor spoke. And yet he loved her, his heart quickened at the thought of her. And the two of them were like Adam and Eve, alone with the stars and the water on this dark uninhabited island—and it was not for nothing that she had come to him, and how miserable she must have been in that hotel room when he had drunk himself into a stupor and gone away, deserting her!

A bitter alienation, an estrangement from the world came over him and he wanted nothing and no one. He remembered that wild animals when they are sick go off and hide in some far-away place in the forest, there to cure themselves by means of some mysterious herb or else to die. He regretted that it was the fall and the weather was so chilly, that he was in boots and a sweater—how nice, if it were summer, to find a corner of this or some other island, with rocks, sand, and clear water, and to lie all day in the sun and to think of nothing. And to walk barefoot. And fish. And watch sunsets. He realized that he was boundlessly weary—of himself, his thoughts, his corroding doubts, of getting drunk —and that altogether he was ill.

'Nice to go to the south, somewhere by the sea . . .' he thought nostalgically as he got up. Leaving the pier and turning his back on the lake, he again came face to face with the enormous ancient church and the small hotel sheltering beside it. The windows of the hotel shone brightly while the church was dark, locked up, and strange to him. Yet there was something masterful and commanding about the church, something which aroused thoughts of history and of the greatness of the people—and also of quietness and solitude.

'*Seg-Pogost*,'[1] he recalled the name of the island and the church. '*Seg-Pogost.*'

He walked up to the house and stood on the steps, peering into the darkness, trying to guess at what for so many centuries without him had lived its own life—the genuine life of the earth, the water, and the people. But he could make out nothing except the dim radiance of the surrounding waters and the few cosmically gleaming tatters of sky in the rifts between the clouds, and so he went inside.

The room was brightly lit by a paraffin lamp. The stove roared and crackled and there was a smell of baked potatoes. Vika was flushed and busy, the whole place had acquired a friendly, lived-in air, and everything in it—the blouses and dresses hanging up or flung on the bed, the black gloves on the bedside table, the powder compact with a zip— told of the presence of a young woman and gave off a smell of scent.

'Where were you?' Vika asked with a quiver of her eyebrows. 'I looked for you.'

Ageyev said nothing and went into the kitchen to wash. There he spent some time inspecting his stubble in the mirror but decided not to shave and only washed, cheerfully clattering the things on the washstand and drying himself on the warm rough towel; then he came back, lay down, put his boots on the headboard, stretched, and lit a cigarette.

'Come and eat,' said Vika.

They ate in silence. Clearly Vika was delighted with her

[1] *Seg*: a Finnish corruption of St Serge; *Pogost*: churchyard.

surroundings and her only trouble was Ageyev. The kettle purred and whistled on the stove.

'How long is your leave?' Ageyev asked abruptly.

'Ten days,' Vika sighed. 'Why?'

'Nothing ...'

'Three days gone,' thought Ageyev.

Again there was a long silence. When they had their tea it was time for bed. Vika blushed hotly and looked in desperation at Ageyev. He looked away and frowned, then got up, lit a cigarette, and walked over to the window. He too was blushing and glad that Vika could not see it. There were rustling sounds behind him; finally Vika couldn't stand it and begged him:

'Do put out the light!'

Without looking at her, Ageyev blew out the flame of the oil lamp, quickly undressed, got into his bed and turned to the wall. 'Just try and come to me,' he thought. But Vika didn't come. She lay so still that he couldn't even hear her breathing.

Some twenty minutes went by; neither of them was asleep and they both knew it. It was dark in the room and the sky outside the window was black. The wind rose and buffeted the walls. Suddenly the window curtain was lit up for a brief moment. Ageyev thought at first that someone had walked past and shone a torch on the wall and the window, but a few seconds later there came a low rumble of thunder.

'There's a storm,' Vika said softly, sitting up in bed and looking at the dark window. 'An autumn storm.'

After another flash and rumble, the wind died down and it began at once to pelt with rain, water gurgled in the rainpipe.

'It's raining,' said Vika. 'I like it when it rains. I like thinking when it rains.'

'You couldn't keep quiet, could you?' Ageyev lit a cigarette and blinked: his eyes were smarting.

'You know what? I'm leaving,' said Vika, and Ageyev felt her hating him. 'I'm going by the first boat. You're nothing but an egoist. I've been thinking and thinking these past two days—what are you? What's the matter with you? Well, I know now—you're just selfish. You talk about the people,

about art, but all you think about is yourself and absolutely
no one else . . . You don't need anyone. It's revolting! Why
on earth did you ask me to come, why? I know why—to
pat you on the back and say, "yes, darling," isn't that it?
Well, my lad, you can look for another victim. I'm ashamed
to think how I pestered the Dean of the Faculty and told lies
about my father being ill . . .'

She burst into loud sobs.

'Shut up, you fool!' Ageyev said miserably, realizing it
was all over. 'And get out of here, go away, the sooner the
better!'

He got up and sat in front of the window, leaning his
elbows on the bedside table. It was still raining and there
was something large, dark and quivering on the ground outside—he looked at it for a long time before he realized it
was a puddle. He wanted to cry, to blink his eyes and rub
them with his sleeve as he did when he was a child, but it
was many years since he'd been able to cry.

Vika had buried her head in her pillow and lay sobbing
and catching her breath, while Ageyev sat still, breaking
matchsticks and crumbling cigarette ends in the ash-tray. At
first he had felt sick and cold with misery and disgust. Now
this had passed, he had somehow risen above it, aloof, de-
tached from pettiness, and feeling sorry for everyone, quiet
and saddened by the insurmountable resistance of the
human mass. And yet everything deep inside him was boil-
ing, seething, hurt, and he could not be silent, he could no
longer smile his condescending smile or get out of things
with his loathsome 'Ugh!' He had to say something.

But he said nothing, he only thought, though he wasn't
really thinking about anything, only keeping quiet and glancing through the window at the dark, quivering puddle outside. There was a singing, a jangling in his head as if he
was ill and had a temperature, and he saw before him
an endless procession of people walking silently through the
halls of a gallery, their expressions enigmatic, elusive, and
sorrowful. 'Why sorrowful?' he was held up by the thought;
'I've got it wrong somehow.' But he was at once distracted

and began to think of higher things, of the highest, the loftiest of all, as it seemed to him.

He was thinking that whatever happened he would do what he must. And that no one would stop him. And that in the end this would be to his credit.

He stood up, and without dressing, with swollen veins in his temples, went out on to the porch. There he stood and spat—for some reason his mouth was full of sweetish saliva, it kept filling with it and he kept spitting it out, and there was a lump in his throat, choking him.

'It's all over!' he muttered softly. 'To hell with it. It's all over.'

All next day Ageyev slumped on his bed with his face to the wall. He would go to sleep and wake up and hear Vika walk about the room and round the house. She called him to lunch and to dinner but he lay with his teeth angrily clenched and not opening his eyes, in a kind of stupor, until he fell asleep again.

By the evening his muscles were aching and he was forced to get up. Vika was out; Ageyev went to find the landlady.

'Would you give me the key of the boat,' he begged her. 'I have to go to the shop for some cigarettes.'

The landlady gave him the key of the padlock, told him where to find the oars, and showed him the direction in which to row.

There was a headwind, the oars were heavy and awkward, the boat was heavy too, though so fine to look at, and Ageyev had blisters on his hands by the time he reached the other island.

He bought cigarettes, a bottle of vodka, and some snacks, and walked back to the mooring-stage.

On the way he was overtaken by a stocky, bow-legged fisherman in a winter hat and with a red face.

'Hello, there,' said the fisherman, drawing level with him and looking him over. 'You an artist? From Seg-Pogost?'

He had parcels wrapped in newspaper which he held

111

carefully in both hands and two bottles of vodka stuffed in the pockets of his jacket.

'We've got a party on today! After our steam bath,' he gave the news joyfully as to an old friend. 'Shall we have one for the road?'

The fisherman clumped across into his boat which had an outboard-motor with a bright-green casing, produced four bottles (two out of his trouser pockets), and carefully put three of them down on the tarpaulin in the prow; the fourth he opened at once and after fumbling for an empty jam jar and rinsing it in the lake poured Ageyev a drink. Ageyev drank it down and chewed a biscuit. The fisherman poured one out for himself and climbed ashore.

'Glad to know you,' he said cheerfully. 'Been here long?'

'Only since yesterday,' said Ageyev, inspecting him deliberately.

'Painting the church?' he winked.

'Whatever I find.'

'You should come over and visit our work-gang,' the fisherman offered, the vodka rushing to his head. 'Got a woman with you? We've got women,' he spread his hands, 'like that! See? You'll want to paint the lot, see?'

He went back to the boat for the bottle they had started and poured Ageyev another drink.

'Let's finish it up, shall we?'

'Actually, I've got my own,' said Ageyev, also getting out a bottle.

'We'll drink yours when you come to us,' said the fisherman. 'It's not far; you just say when you want to come and we'll fetch you by motor-boat. We like artists, they're all right. We had a professor from Leningrad staying a while back. He said, never in my life, he said, have I seen people like you!' The fisherman roared with laughter. 'We'll give you fish soup. You'll have a good time, when the girls start making a row it goes on all night. It's a fine life.'

'Where do you fish?' asked Ageyev smiling.

'Off Kizhm Island, but don't worry, we'll fetch you. Or if you think of coming over by yourself just ask for Stepan's gang—that's me, Stepan, get it? Soon as you're out of the reefs, turn left, past the lighthouse, and you'll see the island. You can't miss it. There they'll tell you.'

'I'll certainly come!' Ageyev said happily.

'That's right! You come along! You respect me, right? You treat me like a human being, right? Well, that's all there is to it! That's the lot . . . That's settled then. Right? Well, that's all. Good-bye for now, I've got to run, the boys are waiting . . .'

He climbed over into his boat, unmoored it, pushed off, and started the engine. It set up a thin buzzing. He threw himself into the bows but they reared up all the same; using the tiller the fisherman steered the boat into deep water and skimmed away, leaving a white frothing arc on the water behind him.

Smiling to himself, Ageyev got into his boat and started back. He now sat facing the sunset and he couldn't help stopping and resting on his oars from time to time, to watch the colours of the sky and the lake. Half-way to Seg-Pogost there was a small island, and when he rounded it the wind died down and the water lay still and heavy like molten gold.

In the perfect silence and the calm Ageyev shipped his oars and turned round to look at the church. A rain-cloud, almost like a black wall, rose in the east, while from the west the sun was shedding its last rays, and everything they lit—the island, the church, the windmill, the old farm— seemed, against the cloud, to glow with a particularly omi- nous red. Far away on the side of the horizon from which the cloud was moving, hung tattered drapes of rain and a huge rainbow shone funereally.

Ageyev settled himself more comfortably in the boat, had another drink, and nibbling a biscuit sat looking at the church. The sun was setting, the cloud was drawing nearer, it already overshadowed almost everything in sight, the rain had by now reached Seg-Pogost. The boat was drifting slightly with the current.

But around Ageyev all was as yet calm and still, while in the west the sky burned with a wide band of misty red flung around the setting sun.

Ageyev sat examining the church and felt like painting it. He was thinking that it was not, of course, only three centuries old, but immeasurably older; it was as old as the earth and the stones. The other thing he couldn't get out of his mind was the image of the jolly fisherman, and he felt like painting him as well.

When he turned to the west the sun had set. The rain had come at last. He pulled his hood over his head and picked up the oars. The heavy rain was for some reason warm and gay, and fish jumped all around him as he rowed.

Coming up to the landing-stage at full tilt, Ageyev saw Vika. She stood motionless in the rain, a plastic raincoat thrown over her shoulders, and watched him as he moored and padlocked the boat, took out the oars and the rucksack with his purchases and stuffed the half-empty bottle into his pocket.

'You can look!' Ageyev thought cheerfully as he walked in silence to the house.

Vika stayed at the pier. Without turning to look at him she continued to watch the lake in the afterglow and the rain.

Coming into the warm room Ageyev saw that her things were no longer around and her suitcase stood by the door. 'Ah!' he said, and lay down. The rain drummed on the roof. Calm and comfortable after his vodka, he shut his eyes and dozed off. He soon woke up; it was not yet dark but the rain had stopped and the sky had cleared and had a cold, high radiance.

Ageyev yawned and went to find the landlady. Taking from her the keys of the church, he went inside the fence which surrounded the churchyard, crossed it, stepping between old tombs, unlocked the door of the bell tower, and started up the dark, narrow, creaking stairs.

There was a smell of jackdaw droppings and of dry wood, and it was dark, but the higher he climbed the more light there was and the cleaner the air. At last he reached the platform of the belfry, his heart wobbly and his legs weak from the sensation of height.

At first, as he climbed on to the platform through the

trap-door, he saw only the sky through the arches—high up, with a few fleecy clouds in it and the first large stars, and with light in its depth from the blue rays of the long extinguished sun.

Then as he looked down he saw another sky, as enormous and as light as the one above. Stretching to the horizon on all sides, the whole immeasurable mass of the surrounding water was luminous with reflected light, and the small islands on it were like clouds.

From the moment Ageyev sat down on the balustrade, his arm hooked round a pillar, he never moved again until it was quite dark and Cassiopeia stood out in all its pearly brilliance, and later, after he came down, he walked round and round the church along the path, peering at it this way and that and sighing.

When he came home, the stove was crackling once again. Vika was cooking supper, but she was quiet and already far away.

'Is the boat coming soon? Did you find out?' asked Ageyev.

'At 11 o'clock, I think,' Vika said, after a silence.

Ageyev's heart lurched, he wanted to say something, to ask her some question, but he said nothing and only dragged his paintbox from under the bed, set out paint tubes and small bottles of turpentine on the window-sill and the bed, sorted his brushes, and began to knock at a set of stretchers. Vika kept glancing at him in amazement.

They sat down to supper in silence like the first time, and looked each other in the eyes. Ageyev saw Vika's dry lips, her face suddenly so dear to him. His heart gave another lurch and he realized that the time to say good-bye had come.

He got a bottle of vodka from under the bed and poured out for Vika and himself.

'Well . . .' he said huskily, and cleared his throat. 'Here's to our parting!'

Vika put down her glass without drinking, leaned back in her chair and thus, with her head thrown back, looked at him from under lowered eyelids. Her face was quivering, a

vein was throbbing in her neck, her lips moved, it was more
than Ageyev could bear to see. He felt hot. Getting up, he
opened the window and leaned out for a breath of the strong
night air.

'It's stopped raining,' he said, coming back to the table
and taking another drink. 'It isn't raining any more.'

'You don't need any money?' asked Vika. 'I've got too
much. I brought a lot, you know, thinking . . .' She bit her
lip and smiled pitifully.

'No, I don't,' said Ageyev. 'I'll stop drinking now.'

'I still think you're wrong,' Vika said sadly. 'You're just
ill. If you gave up drinking everything would go right.'

'Oh, would it,' he grinned. 'I'd have a one-man show at
once, would I? Cheers!' He drank again. 'And the opportunists would realize they're no artists, right?'

'Where were you this evening?' Vika asked, after a silence.

'Over there,' he gestured vaguely. 'Upstairs. Calling on
God.'

'You won't be coming to Moscow soon?' she asked again,
looking at the paints, brushes, and easels scattered round the
room.

'Not yet, no,' he said, seeing in his imagination the fisher-
women he would get to know, their legs, their breasts. Their
eyes. Seeing them at their work, with clenched teeth and red
arms as they hauled the nets. 'In about a month, I should
think. Or later still. I'll have a go at painting the fisher-
folk. And the water.' He paused. 'And the sky. That's how
it is, old girl.'

Vika went outside to listen for the boat.

'It's too early,' she said, coming back. After looking at herself thoughtfully in the mirror she got her scarf out of her
suitcase, put it on her head and tied the ends under her
chin. Then she sat down and clenched her hands between
her knees. She sat in silence, her head bowed low, as if she
were sitting at a station, as if Ageyev were unknown to her;
her thoughts were far away. Her hair had golden lights under
the chiffon scarf. Ageyev lay on the bed, squinting, examining her with curiosity and smoking nervously.

'I can't stand it,' said Vika with a sigh. 'I'll go to the pier.'

She got up, sighing again, stared for a few seconds fixedly, unblinking, at the lamp, and put on her coat. Ageyev swung his legs to the floor and sat up.

'Well, all right,' he said. '*Good-bye*,[1] old girl! Like me to see you off? . . .'

Vika went to get her identity card from the landlady. Ageyev took a quick drink, snorted, pulled a face and began to dress, looking attentively at his shaking hands and hearing Vika's and the landlady's voices behind the partition. He picked up the suitcase and went out on to the porch. The steps, the handrail, the plankway to the pier, were still damp from the recent rain. He waited for Vika to come out and walked down. She followed him, her heels tapping on the planks.

When they came to the pier Ageyev put the suitcase on the ground and Vika immediately sat down on it, shrank into herself, and froze into stillness. Ageyev shivered with cold and turned up his collar. Suddenly, out of the dead, unnatural silence of the night there came the high, robust sound of a plane. As it approached, it grew louder, stronger, but at the same time lower in tone, more velvety, muffled, as if someone were ceaselessly drawing a bow over the strings of a cello, gradually lowering the peg, until at last it receded, dying down to a low belly rumble.

Once again there was dead silence. After stamping about next to Vika, Ageyev moved away and climbed the bank. He paused at the top, then walked a few steps towards the southern tip of the island and looked round.

The stars were burning steadily overhead, while all over the reefs on the water below were small red and white lights gleaming and blinking on buoys and markers. Suddenly it was as if a breath rushed through the sky; the stars blinked and shuddered. The sky grew black, shuddered again and rose, filling with blue trembling light. Ageyev turned to look at the north and immediately saw its origin. From behind the church—from behind its silent blackness—there came, spreading its beams and swaying, billowing, folding in and swelling out, the faint, pale-blue-golden radiance of the

[1] *Good-bye* in English in the text.

Northern Lights. Whenever they flared out everything—the lake, the shore, the stones, and the wet grass—shone, and the church stood out in firm silhouette; when it faded everything became diminished, and obscure, and vanished.

The earth was turning. Ageyev suddenly felt it with his legs and his heart as it turned and flew, together with its lakes, cities, people and their hopes—turned and flew, ringed with light, into frightening infinity. And here he stood upon this earth, this island, in the silent light of the night, and Vika was leaving him. Adam was being left by Eve—and not at some uncertain future time but now, at once. And it was like death, which you can laugh at from a distance but cannot even bear to think about when it is close beside you.

He couldn't bear it and walked quickly back to the landing-stage, feeling his boots getting soaked through in the wet grass, seeing nothing in the darkness but knowing that now they were black and shiny.

When he came back to the pier the lantern was already shining on a post, the old woman stood yawning on the steps below, while from beyond a low hill in the north came a new beam, trembling like the Aurora but warmer in tone. The beam shifted, there came the quick noises of paddles, and suddenly, high and resonant, the ship's siren, echoing on and on from island to island.

'Did you see the Northern Lights? It was that, wasn't it?' Vika asked in a quick and low voice. She was excited and no longer sitting on her suitcase but standing by the railings.

'Yes, I saw,' Ageyev cleared his throat.

The ship wheeled into sight round a bend and could now be heard more clearly. The small star of its searchlight shone brightly in the bow. Now the light reached the landing-stage and the lamp glistened on the planks. The engines stopped and the ship drifted on of its own momentum towards the pier. The old woman shielded her eyes with her hand from the brilliant light, peering at something on board. Turning his back on the searchlight Ageyev saw its beam tremble smokily on the beautiful old farm as if spotlighting an antique.

As the steamer pulled alongside the searchlight turned and flooded the pier with a dazzling milky brightness. Vika and Ageyev watched silently as the ship was moored. A sailor on deck flung the end of the cable to the old woman. The old woman unhurriedly slipped the loop over a bollard. The sailor bent down and wound the cable in. The cable tautened and creaked and the pier shuddered. The steamer softly bumped against it. The sailor let down the gangway and stood under the lamp, checking the ticket of some passenger who was getting off. At last he let him through and turned to Vika and Ageyev.

'Coming aboard?' he asked uncertainly.

'Well, off with you,' said Ageyev, giving Vika's shoulder a careless pat. 'All the best!'

Her lips trembled.

'Good-bye,' she said, and climbed on deck, her shoes tapping on the gangway.

The boat was almost empty, the lower deck dimly lit and the cabin portholes dark. Either there was no one in the cabins or the passengers were asleep. Steam hissed between the ship's side and the pier and floated up in transparent puffs.

Vika went below without looking back and vanished in the ship's bowels. The siren shrieked hurriedly—one long and three short blasts, the old woman slipped the noose off the bollard, the gangway was pulled up, the ventilators clanged shut on deck—and the boat, a warm, familiar, breathing creature, the only thing alive in the cold night, was pulling out, gurgling with its paddles and whirling sharply right.

The old woman yawned again, muttered that the Northern Lights were early this year and this meant a hard winter, picked up her lantern and walked up the bank, throwing a patch of light in front of her, smearing yellow light over her boots and carrying on her left side a big un-

steady shadow which, as she swung the lantern, leapt from
the bank over the pier into the lake.

Ageyev stood still smoking a cigarette, and walked back
to the warm hotel. The Northern Lights were still flashing
but were now faint and all of the same colour—white.

translated by Manya Harari

Half-way to the Moon

VASILI AKSYONOV

'Some coffee?'

'Yes.'

'Turkish?'

'Eh?'

'Turkish coffee.' the waitress crowed and flounced away between the tables.

'She's nothing to write home about,' Kirpichenko consoled himself as he watched her go.

'Fuss about nothing!' he thought, wincing from his headache. 'Fifty minutes left. Any moment they'll be calling the flight and I'll get the hell out of this place. Some town, I must say. What a dump. It's no Moscow. There may be those who like it, but they can have it as far as I'm concerned. To hell with it! Maybe it'll look different next time.'

He'd been doing some really hard drinking—not what you might call a real binge, but they'd got pretty tight. For three solid days. All on account of that swine Banin and his precious sister. They'd really messed him up, and all on his own hard-earned roubles!

Kirpichenko had run across Banin three days earlier at the airfield in Yuzhny. He hadn't even known they'd both got leave at the same time. He hadn't really much time for him. At the lumber camp there'd always been a lot of fuss about him, with people shouting all the time: 'Banin, Banin! Take your cue from Banin'—but Kirpichenko never took much notice of him. He knew the name, of course, and he knew who the fellow was—Banin, the electrician—but by and large he didn't stand out in a crowd despite all the fuss kicked up about him on the big holidays. But a fat lot of use Banin was!

There were fellows at the lumber camp who did just as good a job as Banin—they could run circles around him—but the bosses are always the same: when they pick out one man and start a song-and-dance about him, there's no reason for envying such a fellow, he's fit only for pity. There was a fellow called Sinitsyn at Bayukly—drove a tractor like Kirpichenko. The journalists took to him and gave him the full treatment. At first he kept all the newspaper cuttings, but then he couldn't stand it any longer and cleared out to Okha. But Banin didn't mind and put up with it all. Neat little fellow he was, and always on his toes—seemed just an ordinary sort who kept very much to himself. Last year they brought 200 girls from the mainland to the cannery—seasonal workers to gut the fish. The boys went off to see them and were climbing on the truck, yelling and shouting . . . Then they saw Banin sitting in a corner inside as quiet as a mouse, there'd been neither sight nor sound from him.

'Oh, it's Banin, for God's sake,' they said.

At Yuzhny airfield Banin pounced on Kirpichenko as if he were his best friend. He was choking with delight, he shouted that he was terribly pleased, that he had this sister in Khabarovsk, and that she had some girl friends who were really quite something. He began to embroider the whole thing in detail till Kirpichenko started to feel dizzy. After the batch of girls had left the cannery, Valeri Kirpichenko had spent the whole winter without seeing more than two women —or rather two old hags: the one who kept the time-sheets and the cook.

In the plane Banin kept shouting to the crew:

'Hey there, you pilots! Shovel on a bit more coal!'

You could hardly recognize the fellow, what with all those wisecracks . . .

The house where this sister of Banin's lived was almost buried in a snowdrift. The hump-backed street had obviously been cleared by special machines, but the piles of snow had not been taken away, and they almost hid the tiny cot-

Half-way to the Moon

tages from view. It was as if the cottages were in a trench. In the crackling, frosty air there were blue columns of smoke above the chimneys, and aerials and poles with boxes for the starlings stuck out at all angles. It was just a country lane to look at. It was even difficult to believe that there was a trolley-bus route along the highway on the hill.

Kirpichenko had been a bit dazed back in the airport when he saw a long row of cars with green lights in front of a restaurant with a plate-glass wall; you could make out the prim dance-band through the frost patterns. In the shops on the main street he'd really let himself go. He pulled out green fifty-rouble notes, laughed loudly, shoved bottles into his pockets and swept up a whole armful of tinned goods. Banin was tickled pink and laughed even more than Kirpichenko, and just kept picking up cheeses and tinned goods, then he had a talk with one of the managers and took a lot of salami. Banin and Kirpichenko drove to the cottage in a taxi loaded with all kinds of food and bottles of Chechen-Ingush cognac. You might say they didn't come to that sister of his empty-handed.

Kirpichenko went into the room, his shaggy fur hat touching the ceiling, put the stuff down on the white-quilted bed, straightened up, and caught sight of his red, thin, and cross-looking face in a mirror.

Larisa, Banin's sister, who looked like a plump little nurse, was already unbuttoning his overcoat and saying:

'Any friends of my brother are friends of mine.'

Then she put on a coat and boots, and went outside.

Banin got busy with a corkscrew and knife while Kirpichenko looked around. The room was decently furnished with a sideboard and mirror, a chest-of-drawers and a radiogram. A picture of Voroshilov, taken before the war (without epaulets and with his marshal's stars on the lapels), was hanging above the chest. Next to it was a framed certificate: *'To First Class Marksman of the Guard for proficiency in military and political training. From the Administration of the North-Eastern Corrective Labour Camps.'*

'Dad's certificate,' Banin said.

123

'What, you mean he was a concentration-camp guard?'

'He was, but now he's had it,' sighed Banin. 'Dead.'

But he soon cheered up and started to play some records. They were nothing very new: 'Rio Rita', 'The Black Sea Gull', and some kind of French tune with three men singing in harmony as splendidly as if they'd been round the whole wide world and seen things you'd never see yourself.

Larisa came back with a girl friend called Toma. She started setting the table and kept running to and from the kitchen, bringing gherkins and mushrooms, while Toma sat in a corner, just sat there stock-still with her hands on her knees. Kirpichenko didn't know how things would turn out with her and tried not to look at her, but every time he did look he felt dizzy.

> *'We're caught in winter's icy grip,*
> *So now's the time to have a nip,'*

Banin said cheerfully, but he was nervous. 'Supper is served, ladies and gentlemen.'

Kirpichenko was smoking long cigarettes called 'Forty Years of the Soviet Ukraine' and blowing smoke-rings. Larisa was giggling and threading them on her little finger. It was stuffy in the low room. Kirpichenko's feet had got damp in his felt boots and it was probably from them that the steam came. Banin danced with Toma, who didn't say a word all evening. He was whispering something to her and she gave a crooked smile without opening her mouth. She was a well-built girl with pink underwear showing through her nylon blouse. Before Kirpichenko's eyes everything swam in dark orange circles—the walls, Voroshilov's picture, the little porcelain elephants on the chest-of-drawers. The smoke rings he had blown were swirling about, and Larisa was making some sort of signs with her fingers.

Banin and Toma went into another room. The spring lock clicked quietly behind them.

'Ha! ha! ha!' laughed Larisa. 'But why didn't you dance, Valeri? You should have.'

The record ended and there was silence. Larisa looked at him, screwing up her slanting brown eyes. There were muffled squeals from the next room.

'You've got the bread and butter, Valeri,' Larisa sniggered. 'But where's the jam?' And Kirpichenko suddenly saw that she was getting on for thirty and that she had been around.

She came over to him and whispered: 'Let's dance.'

'But I'm wearing felt boots,' he said.

'Doesn't matter, come on.'

He got up. She put on a record, and the three French boys struck up their chorus again in the room, which smelled of tomatoes and Chechen-Ingush cognac. They sang about how they had been round the whole wide world and seen things you would never see.

'Not that one,' Kirpichenko said hoarsely.

'Why not?' shouted Larisa. 'It's a real good record! Right in the groove!'

She started whirling round the room, with her skirt swishing around her legs. Kirpichenko took the record off and put on 'Rio Rita'. Then he strode over to Larisa and seized her by the shoulders.

That's what it's always like when fingers stroke your neck in the dark, and it seems as if they're the fingers of the moon, whatever cheap tart might be lying next to you . . . all the same, afterwards, when these fingers touch your neck . . . and you ought to send her packing . . . you think . . . but what don't you think with the moon high up and looking like a broken egg-yolk through the frosted window? But it never does happen, and don't kid yourself that it ever will. You're already twenty-nine and you've had your ups and downs in this lovely life, but when there are fingers on your neck in the dark, you think it's . . .

'When were you born?' the woman asked.

'In thirty-two.'

'You're a driver, are you?'

'Yes.'

'Earn much?'

Valeri lit a match and saw her round face with its slanting brown eyes.

'Why do you want to know?'

Next morning Banin was shuffling about the room in warm Chinese underwear. He was squeezing gherkin juice into a glass and throwing the wrinkled skins into a dish. Toma sat in a corner, as neat and quiet as on the night before. After breakfast she and Larisa went off to work.

'Proper good time we had, eh, Valeri?' said Banin with a fawning laugh. 'OK then, let's go to the cinema.'

They saw three films in a row and then called at the store, where Kirpichenko really let rip again. He kept pulling out red banknotes and piling cheeses and provisions into Banin's arms.

It had gone on like this for three days and nights, but this morning, after the girls had left, Banin had suddenly said:

'So you're one of the family now, Valeri?'

Kirpichenko choked on the gherkin juice he was drinking for his hangover.

'Wha-at!'

'What do you mean, "what"?' Banin yelled. 'Do you sleep with that sister of mine or don't you? Come on, tell me when we're going to celebrate the wedding, or else I'll report you—for immoral behaviour—see what I mean?'

From right across the table Kirpichenko hit him on the side of the face. Banin went crashing into a corner, jumped up straight away and picked up a chair.

'You bastard!' Kirpichenko snarled and went towards him. 'Think I'm going to marry the first slut that comes along ...'

'You concentration-camp rat!' screamed Banin. 'Jail bird!' And he threw the chair at him.

And now Kirpichenko really showed him what was what. Banin snatched up his sheepskin coat and rushed outside. Kirpichenko's teeth were chattering, he was so furious and upset. He dragged out his suitcase, threw his belongings into it, put on his raincoat and his fur overcoat on top of that, pulled out of his pocket a photograph of himself (wearing a tie and his very best cowboy-style shirt), quickly wrote

126

on it '*To Larisa, in fond memory*', put it on the pillow in Larisa's room—and left the house. In the yard Banin, spluttering and cursing, was untying a savage dog. Kirpichenko kicked the dog away and went out through the gate . . .

Well, how do you like the coffee?' the waitress asked.

'Not bad, it's working,' sighed Kirpichenko, and patted her hand.

'Take it easy,' smiled the waitress.

Then their flight was called and it was time for the passengers to take their seats.

Light-heartedly Kirpichenko marched towards the airfield with long, powerful strides. 'Onward, onward, ever onward!' he thought. What's the point of getting leave once in a month of Sundays if you spend it stuck in a shack on a diet of mushrooms and cheese? There are fellows who spend their whole holiday stuck in that kind of cottage, but he wasn't that stupid. He'd go to Moscow, buy three suits and a pair of Czech shoes in the State Universal Stores, then on, on to the Black Sea—where he'd eat Crimean pastries and lounge around in beach pyjamas.

At that moment he seemed to see himself through someone else's eyes—big and strong, in an overcoat with a fur coat on top, in a muskrat hat and fur boots, striding along like nobody's business. A woman he'd had an affair with a couple of years ago said he had a face like a Red Indian Chief. She was the leader of a geological expedition, of all things. She was a good girl, this Anna Petrovna, a university lecturer or something of the sort. She wrote him letters and he wrote back: 'Greetings, dear Anna Petrovna! The writer of these lines is your old friend Valeri Kirpichenko . . .' all kinds of fancy things like that.

A big crowd of passengers had already gathered by the turnstiles. Not far away Larisa was hopping around. Her face was white with a touch of blue, her lips were bright red, and the brooch on her collar, shaped like a running stag, looked terribly stupid.

'What did you come for?' asked Kirpichenko.

'T-to see you off,' Larisa could hardly get the words out.

'Oh, cut it out,' he said. 'You and your darling brother messed me up for three days . . . That's fine, but don't try on any of that love stuff.'

Larisa burst into tears and Valeri got scared.

'Now, now, don't take on . . .'

'All right,' she snivelled. 'All right, so that's the way it was . . . OK . . . I know what you think of me . . . and you're right . . . But can't I love you if I want to?'

'Cut it out.'

'No, I won't, I won't!' Larisa almost shouted. 'Valeri, you . . .' She came up close to him. 'You're not like the others . . .'

'I'm just the same as everyone else, except that perhaps . . .' And Kirpichenko slowly stretched his lips in a smile.

Larisa turned away and began crying even more. Her pitiful little body was shaking all over.

'Now, now, don't take on . . .' Kirpichenko said. He was very upset and he stroked her shoulder.

Then the crowd began moving on to the runway. Kirpichenko left without looking back. He was thinking that he felt sorry for Larisa and that he'd come to feel at home with her, though actually that was something which happened to him with any girl on account of his idiotic character. Afterwards he always forgot and everything went back to normal. Back to normal, and that was that.

He walked among the crowd of passengers, gazing at the huge aeroplane gleaming in the sunlight, and very soon he forgot everything—the horror of his three days' stay here and those fingers on his neck. He wasn't for sale at that price. That's the way it always had been. He couldn't be bought and he couldn't be broken. He hadn't only had to do with tarts, he'd had some really fine women too. That university lecturer, for instance, was a real honey. They'd all fallen for him, and Valeri knew that this was brought about not by his cruelty, but by something else—perhaps because he didn't talk much, perhaps because each woman wanted to be something special to him, or because they could obviously sense that he was like a blind man groping his way in the dark. But he always said to himself: 'You won't catch me with these little tricks. You won't break me down. The thing's happened and it's over. And we're back to normal. Back to normal again.'

The aeroplane was terrifyingly huge. It was as huge and heavy as a warship. Kirpichenko had never flown in such a plane before, and this one simply took his breath away. The thing he really liked was machinery. He climbed up a high gangway. An air hostess in a dark blue uniform and cap looked at his ticket and told him where his seat was. The seat was up front, but there was some character already sitting in it, a fellow with spectacles and a cloth cap.

'Come on, beat it,' said Kirpichenko quickly, showing his ticket to the man in spectacles.

'Couldn't you take my seat?' the man asked. 'I get sick at the back.'

'Clear out, I tell you,' Kirpichenko barked at him.

'You might be more polite,' said the man in spectacles, looking hurt. For some reason he didn't get up.

Kirpichenko yanked the man's hat off and threw it right back towards where he should have been sitting. What he meant was—and he couldn't have made it clearer—'Next time, take the seat marked on your ticket.'

'Hey, why are you making trouble?' the air hostess asked.

'Take it easy,' Kirpichenko said.

Completely nonplussed, the man in spectacles went to find his hat, and Kirpichenko sat down in his proper seat.

He took off his overcoat and put it at his feet, to stake out his claim, so to speak.

The passengers were coming into the plane one by one, there seemed to be no end of them. Inside light music was playing. Sunlight was pouring in through the door. The air hostesses were bustling up and down the aisle, all of them wore the same kind of blue uniform, and they had long legs and high-heeled shoes. Kirpichenko read the newspaper. Stuff about disarmament and Berlin, about preparations for the football championship in Chile, and the way to preserve the snow-cover for winter crops.

Some peasant woman with a shawl round her took the seat by the window, and a rosy-cheeked sailor took the place next to Kirpichenko. He kept making jokes:

'Made your will, lady . . . ?' And he shouted at the stewardess. 'Miss, who do we hand our wills to?'

Funny how Kirpichenko was always running into these jokers!

At last the door was slammed and a red notice came on: *'No smoking. Fasten your seat-belts,'* together with something in English which might have been the same thing or something else. It could have been the opposite: *'Please smoke. You need not fasten your seat-belts.'* Kirpichenko didn't know English.

A woman's voice spoke through the loudspeaker:

'May I have your attention, please! Your Captain welcomes passengers aboard the Soviet airliner TU 114. Our giant aircraft is bound from Khabarovsk to Moscow. We will be cruising at an altitude of 30,000 feet at a speed of 440 miles an hour. Our flying time will be eight hours, thirty minutes. Thank you for your attention.' Then she said some gibberish in English.

'That's the stuff,' Kirpichenko said with satisfaction, and winked at the sailor. 'Everything ship-shape.'

'What d'you expect?' said the sailor, just as if the aircraft was his own property and as if he'd laid on the whole thing —the announcements in two languages and all the other stuff.

The plane taxied out for the take-off. The peasant woman was tense in her seat. The airport buildings floated past the window.

'May I have your coat?' the air-hostess asked.

It was the same girl who had ticked him off. He looked at her and went all faint. She was smiling. Her smiling face was bending over him, and her hair—it was dark, no, you couldn't say it was black—it was dark and must be soft. It was neatly done up and looked like fur, fleece, or nylon— like all the treasures in the world. Her fingers touched the sheepskin of his coat, and he'd never seen fingers like that before. Well, he had seen such things in the magazines, but you never got all this together, with such a smile and the voice of the greatest woman in the world. No, such things didn't happen.

'See how she took my coat?' Kirpichenko said to the sailor with a silly smile on his face. The sailor winked back and said proudly:

'They know their stuff, eh?'

She came back and picked up the peasant woman's short fur coat, the sailor's leather jacket and Kirpichenko's other coat. She pressed the whole lot to that wonderful body of hers and said:

'Fasten your seat-belts, comrades.'

The engines roared. The peasant woman almost had a fit and crossed herself on the sly. The sailor mimicked her and looked out of the corner of his eye to see if Kirpichenko was laughing. But he was craning his neck and watching that girl. Then she came back with a tray and gave everyone sweets, or maybe they weren't sweets, but heart pills—or nuggets of gold, for all he knew. Then, when they were airborne, she brought round soft drinks and mineral water, the kind of water which flows only in the highest and purest waterfalls. Then she vanished.

'Play cards?' asked the sailor. 'We might get up a game.'

The red sign went out and Kirpichenko knew it was all right to smoke. He got up and went right up front—into a cubby-hole behind a curtain. Clouds of steam were pouring out of it already.

'Here is some information about our flight,' said a voice on the loudspeaker. 'Altitude: 30,000 feet. Speed: 470 miles an hour. Air temperature outside: $-58°C$. Thank you for your attention.'

Far below a rocky wasteland floated past. It even made Kirpichenko shudder to think that in the icy air way above the cruel, bare earth, this metal cigar was sailing along, full of human warmth, politeness, cigarette smoke, muffled talk and laughter, jokes (the kind you wouldn't tell your sister), mineral water, drops from a waterfall in some fertile region—while he was sitting here and smoking, and somewhere in the tail or maybe in the middle of the plane, there

was a woman of the kind that doesn't really exist, the kind
that's as far away from you as the moon.

He started thinking about his life and remembering things.
He'd never done this before, except when he was spinning
some yarn or other to the boys. But now he thought all of a
sudden: 'My fourth trip right across the country, and the
first at my own expense. Terrific!'

All his previous trips had been paid for by the Government. In 1939, when Valeri was still a kid, all the members
of their kolkhoz in Stavropol suddenly expressed their wish
to be transferred to the Far Eastern Coastal Region. The
journey had taken a long time. He remembered a little of
it—sour milk and sour cabbage soup, with his mother wash-
ing clothes in a corner of the railway truck, and hanging
them out of the window to dry; they flapped like flags out
there and then froze stiff and banged against the side of the
train, while he sang: *'Pilots sit in the sky, as their aeroplanes
fly, and look down on the earth from on high . . .'* His mother
had died during the war, and his father was killed in action
in the Kuriles in 1945. Valeri got seven years of schooling
in an orphanage and was then trained as an apprentice in a
factory school. After that he worked in a mine, and dug coal
for the good old motherland. In 1950 he was called up and
they sent him right across the country again—to the Baltic
Coast this time. They trained him as a driver in the Army,
and when he was demobbed he went to Novorossiisk with a
pal. A year after that he was arrested. Some bastard had
been pinching spare parts from the garage where he
worked, but the cops didn't waste their time on the business and they picked on him as the 'materially responsible
person'. He got three years, and they sent him to Sakhalin.
He spent a year and a half in a camp and was then let out
for good conduct. After that he was cleared and given a
full pardon. Ever since then he had worked in the lumber
camp. He liked the work and the money was good. All he
had to do was tow trailers up to the top of a mountain and
then bring them down the other side with all the brakes on,
drink hard liquor, go to the films, and, in summer, to dances

with the girls at the cannery. He lived in a hostel. He'd lived all his life in hostels, barracks, and dormitories. Nothing but bunks, single-decker and double-decker, plank beds, benches . . . He had no friends, but plenty of 'pals'. People were a bit scared of him and thought twice before they fooled around with him. He'd give you a black eye as soon as look at you. And he was very good at his job. He loved machines, and remembered the things he'd driven as other people remember their friends. There was 'Ivan Willis' (his jeep in the Army), then a haulage truck, then a one-and-a-half tonner, a Tatra, and the Diesel he had now . . . In the towns out there—like Yuzhny, Sakhalinsk, Poronaisk, or Korsakov—he sometimes stopped on a corner and looked up at the windows of the new blocks of flats, at all the posh standard lamps and window-curtains, and it worried him sometimes. He never thought of his age, and had only recently realized that he'd be thirty in a few months' time. In Moscow he would buy himself three suits and a green hat, and go down south like one of those big-shots with briefcases. He had travellers' cheques sewn into his underpants—all the cash in the world. He'd have lots of fun down there. It would really be something.

He got up and went to look for that girl. Where had she gone to? The passengers were all dying for a drink and there she was standing and jabbering in English to some capitalist.

She was chatting with her eyes all screwed up and smiling, and it looked as if she liked gossiping in English. The capitalist was standing right by her. He was tall and scraggy and his hair was close-cropped and grey, though he was quite young. His jacket was undone and there was a thin gold chain running from his belt to a pocket. He had a booming voice, and the words rattled in his mouth as if they were banging into his teeth. Kirpichenko knew all about this kind of small talk:

HE: Let's go to San Francisco and drink whisky, my dear.

SHE: You are going a little too far, sir.

HE: In Singapore, with all those banana and lemon trees . . . Understand?

SHE: Do you really mean it? With the banana trees bending in the breeze?

HE: Then we go up to the hundred-and-second storey, and there's boogie-woogie and jazz.

Kirpichenko went up and jogged the capitalist with his shoulder. The capitalist was taken aback and said: 'I am sorry.'[1] By which he meant, of course: 'Watch out, young fellow, or you'll get it.'

'Take it easy,' said Kirpichenko. 'Peace and friendship, and all that.'

(He knew his politics.)

The capitalist said something to her over Kirpichenko's head. It sounded like: 'Take your choice. It's either him or me: Vladivostok or San Francisco.'

And she said with a smile: 'I know this comrade, and you leave me alone. I am a Soviet woman.'

'What do you want, comrade?' she asked Kirpichenko.

'My throat's sort of dry,' he said. 'Got anything I can drink?'

'Come this way,' she said, and went ahead, as frisky as a lamb. Like something in the films, she was, like a dream. God, how he'd longed for her while he'd been smoking up front there.

She walked ahead like something out of this world, and took him to a kind of buffet, or it might have been her own home, where there was no one else, and where the tall sun shone with quiet fury through a porthole, or perhaps through a window on the eighth floor of a new block of flats. She picked up a bottle and poured the bubbling liquid into a tumbler. She picked up the glass and it blazed with light in the sun. And he looked at the girl, and he wanted to have a kid by her, but he couldn't even imagine doing to her what people do when they want to have children; it was the first time this had happened, and he was suddenly warmed by an unexpected glow of happiness.

'What's your name?' he asked, with the same feeling he always had coming down the mountainside on his tractor—a mixture of fear and a feeling that the worst was over.

[1] In English in the text.

'Tanya,' she answered.

'And I'm Kirpichenko . . . Valeri,' he said, and held out his hand.

She gave him her fingers, and smiled.

'You're not the shy sort,' she said.

'A bit,' he said, feeling crushed.

For a few seconds they looked at each other without speaking. She felt like bursting out laughing. She was trying not to, and so was he, but he couldn't keep it up and smiled as he had surely never done in his life before.

Then someone called her, and she ran down the steps to the lower deck of the plane.

Kirpichenko turned, and saw his smiling face in a mirror. 'What a face,' he thought. 'Pretty grim—like a real thug. But she doesn't seem to worry. I'm sure she's not scared a bit.'

He started back down the aisle and saw the fellow with the specs who'd tried to take his seat. He was lying back with his eyes closed. He had a handsome face, just as if it was cut out of marble.

'Listen, fellow,' said Kirpichenko, prodding his shoulder. 'Take my place if you like.'

He opened his eyes and smiled faintly. 'Thanks, I'm all right where I am . . .'

Perhaps it wasn't the man's first flight in this kind of plane, and he'd taken the seat up front so he could watch the door opening into the cabin and see the members of the crew combing their hair, smoking, laughing, reading newspapers, and taking an occasional look at the instruments.

Tanya began serving dinner. She gave Valeri his tray and looked at him as if he was an old friend.

'Where d'you live, Tanya?' he asked.

'In Moscow,' she answered, and went off.

Kirpichenko ate, and kept thinking that his steak was thicker than other people's, that his apple was larger, and that she had given him more bread. Then she brought tea.

'So you come from Moscow?' he asked again.

'Yes,' she said brightly, and went off.

135

'You're wasting your time, pal,' the sailor said with a grin. 'I bet she's got some smart boy friend waiting for her in Moscow.'

'Don't worry,' said Kirpichenko with a feeling of his own well-being and happiness.

But flights like this don't last for ever, and aeroplanes have a habit of coming down from their lofty heights. A stewardess's tour of duty comes to an end, too, and she finishes all the little chores that go with it. She hands back your coat with her frail little hands and her eyes begin to wander. And everything slowly runs down, like clockwork in a toy, and goes as flat and stale as the girl in the magazine with that ad: 'AEROFLOT, YOUR AIR TRAVEL AGENT'—a real marvel with painted nails, high-heeled shoes, and a smart hair-do all thrown in.

But no, nothing was running down and nothing was going flat, though they were already taxi-ing along the ground . . .

Now there was a great hustle and bustle, but the girl in the blue cap wasn't there any more.

'Don't get in the way, comrade . . .'

'Get a move on there . . .'

'Here she is, boys, it's Moscow . . .'

'Moscow, here we come! . . .'

'Oh, come on, for Christ's sake . . .'

Still not grasping what was happening to him, Kirpichenko left the plane with the sailor, went down the steps and got into a bus. The bus drove over to the airport building and the 'Soviet Liner TU 114, Giant of the Air,' that flying fortress of his dreams, quickly vanished from his sight.

The taxi sped along a broad highway with two traffic lanes. Lorries, vans, and tip-up trucks hugged the side of the road, while passenger vehicles raced along at top speed and overtook them so quickly they might have been standing still. Then Kirpichenko and the sailor caught sight of the pinkish, thousand-eyed apartment blocks of the south-western suburb. The sailor fidgeted in his seat and put his hand on Valeri's shoulder.

'The big city! What do you think?'

'Listen, does that plane fly back now?' Kirpichenko asked.

'Of course. They'll be off tomorrow.'

'With the same crew?'

The sailor gave a mocking whistle.

'Come off it! She's just one of these posh modern girls. There's millions like that in Moscow. No need to go off your rocker.'

'I was only just wondering,' mumbled Kirpichenko.

'Where to, boys?' asked the driver.

'Take us to the State Stores in Red Square,' Kirpichenko blurted out and at once forgot all about the plane.

At the stores he bought three suits straight off—blue, grey, and brown. He kept the brown suit on, and taking his old one, which had been made four years previously by a tailor in Sakhalin, rolled it up in a bundle and left it in a lavatory. The sailor got himself some gabardine for a macintosh and said he would have it made in Odessa. They drank a bottle of champagne apiece in a food shop and did a tour of the Kremlin. Then they went and dined in the National Hotel and ate something with a fancy name—Julienne or something—and drank Georgian wine. There were a lot of girls here who looked like Tanya. Maybe Tanya had been here even. She might have been sitting at their table now and pouring him mineral water, and going off to the kitchen all the time to see how they were getting on with his steak. At any rate, the capitalist from the plane was here. Kirpichenko waved to him, and he stood up and bowed. Then they went out in the street and drank another bottle of champagne each. In Gorky Street, Tanya was all over the place. She skipped in and out of trolley-buses, and ran into shops. She strolled with the teddy boys on the other side of the street, or else smiled from shop windows. Gripping each other firmly by the arm, Kirpichenko and the sailor walked up Gorky Street and smiled. The sailor began humming:

'Madagascar, land of my birth . . .'

It was already dusk, but the lights were not yet on. At the end of the street, on the edge of the world, there was a glow of springtime. Yes, here was the land of dreams come true. They wondered why the girls shied away from them.

Later on they found there were queues for every place that was open, and they couldn't get in anywhere. They began to think about where to spend the night, so they hailed a cab and went to Vnukovo Airport. They took a room with two bunks in the airport hotel: the moment he set eyes on the white sheets, Kirpichenko realized how tired he was. He tore off his new suit and flopped down on the bed.

An hour later he was woken up by the sailor who was rushing round the room, scraping his cheeks with a 'Sputnik' shaver and chortling:

'Get up, Val! I've just got hold of some girls, oh boy! . . . Get up, and let's go! They live right here in the hotel. This is the real thing, believe me, I've got a feel for these things . . . Come on, out of bed! *Ma-da-gascar . . .*'

'Stop clucking around like a hen on a new-laid egg!' said Kirpichenko, taking a cigarette from the bedside-table and lighting it.

'Are you coming or aren't you?' asked the sailor from the doorway.

'Put the lights out,' Kirpichenko said.

The lights went out, and straightaway the moonlit square of the window was outlined against the wall, criss-crossed by the lattice and the swaying shadows of bare branches. It was quiet, apart from a gramophone playing somewhere far away: on the other side of the wall someone asked 'Who's got the six?' and banged on the table with a domino. Then a plane roared past as it came in to land. Kirpichenko smoked and imagined her lying beside him, both of them lying together afterwards, with her fingers stroking his neck. It all seemed to be real and not just make-believe, because everything he hadn't understood in his childhood and his youth— the Siberian hillocks standing out in the pink light of dawn, and melting snow, and tiredness after work, and Saturday and Sunday morning—all these things were Tanya.

'What a business,' he thought, and once again that feeling of well-being and happiness came over him. He was glad that this had happened to him. He was scared of only one thing—that a hundred years would pass and he would forget her face and voice.

The sailor came into the room quietly. He undressed and lay down, took a cigarette from the bedside-table, lit up and sang sadly:

'*Madagascar, land of my birth, Spring comes like every-where on earth* . . . Oh, damn,' he went on angrily. 'What a life! Here today and gone tomorrow . . .'

'How long have you been at sea?' asked Kirpichenko.

'Since 'fifty-seven,' the sailor answered, and started singing again:

> *Madagascar, land of my birth,*
> *Spring comes like everywhere on earth,*
> *We are people, like everyone,*
> *We can love, just like you—*
> *Our skin is black, but our blood is red and true* . . .

'Write down the words for me,' Kirpichenko asked him.

They turned on the light and the sailor gave him the words of this wonderful song. He liked that kind of song very much.

Next day they took their tickets to be endorsed, so that Kirpichenko could go on to Sochi and the sailor to Odessa. They had breakfast. Kirpichenko bought a book by Chekhov, and a magazine at a news-stand.

'Tell you what,' the sailor said. 'My girl has a nice little friend. How about taking a trip into town with them?'

Kirpichenko sat down in a chair and opened his book.

'No, no,' he said. 'You two go off, and I'll sit around here for a bit and read this stuff.'

The sailor semaphored a naval signal: *Message received. Good luck. Am setting course.*

Kirpichenko loafed around the airport all day, but didn't see Tanya. In the evening he saw the sailor off on the flight to Odessa—and they drank a bottle of champagne each. Then he walked the sailor's girl friend to the hostel, went back to the airport ticket office and bought a ticket for the giant TU 114, flight number 901, Moscow to Khabarovsk.

Inside the plane everything was just the same—the signs in two languages and all the rest, but there was no Tanya. It was a different crew. There were some girls like Tanya, every bit as young and pretty, but none of them was in her class. After Tanya this lot came nowhere.

Next morning Kirpichenko was back in Khabarovsk, and an hour later he left for Moscow again in a different plane. But Tanya wasn't on this one either.

So he flew to and fro between Moscow and Khabarovsk, at a height of 30,000 feet and at a speed of 470 miles an hour. The air temperature outside varied from − 50 to − 60°C. All the instruments functioned normally.

By now he knew almost all the stewardesses and quite a few of the pilots on this line by sight; he was afraid they might remember him too.

He thought he might be taken for a spy . . .

He kept changing his suits. He'd do one trip in the blue one, another in the brown, and a third in the grey.

He slit open his underpants, took out his travellers' cheques and put them in the pocket of his coat. They were going fast.

And still there was no sign of Tanya.

There was a fierce sun high up, rising and setting above a snowy wilderness of cloud. There was a moon, which seemed not far away, and in fact it wasn't very far off.

For a while he lost all track of time and space, and he stopped re-setting his watch. Khabarovsk seemed like a Moscow suburb, and Moscow seemed like a new district of Khabarovsk.

He read a great deal. He'd never read so much in his life.

He'd never thought so much in his life.

He'd never cried so much in his life.

He'd never had such a wonderful holiday in his life.

Spring was beginning in Moscow. Drops from those same high and pure waterfalls dripped down his neck. He bought a grey scarf with a large check pattern.

Just in case they might meet, he had got a present ready

Half-way to the Moon

for Tanya—a box of perfume called *'The First of May'* and a length of cloth for a dress.

I ran across him in the Khabarovsk airport building. He was sitting in an armchair with his legs crossed, reading Stanyukovich. A string bag full of oranges was hanging on the arm of the chair. The cover of the book showed a clipper scudding along in a storm with billowing sails.

'You a sailor by any chance?' he asked, after a look at my leather jacket.

'No.'

I stared at his strange, awesome face. He read a bit more and then asked another question:

'Are you sorry you're not a sailor?'

'Of course I am,' I said.

'So am I,' he said with a laugh. 'I've got a friend who's a sailor. Here's a cable he sent me from sea.'

He showed me the cable.

'Aha,' I said.

Then he asked me:

'When were you born?'

'In thirty-two,' I answered.

He beamed all over his face:

'That means we're the same age, you and me.'

It really was a tremendous coincidence and I shook him by the hand.

'I bet you live in Moscow, don't you?' he said.

'You're right,' I answered. 'Moscow it is.'

'I bet you've got a flat, haven't you? And a wife and kid and all that?'

'Right again. Just as you say.'

'What do you say we go and have a meal?'

I was on the point of going with him, but at that moment my flight was called. I was going to Petropavlovsk. We swapped addresses, and I moved off towards the plane. I walked over the airfield, hunched up in the wind and rain and thinking what an odd character he was.

Meanwhile he looked at his watch, picked up his string bag and went out. He took a taxi into town. Both he and the driver had trouble finding that hump-backed country lane because he couldn't remember the name of it. All the houses in this lane looked the same, and there were great big dogs barking in all the yards. He felt a bit lost. In the end he remembered where the place was. He got out of the taxi, hung his string bag with the oranges on the fence, covered it up with a newspaper to stop neighbours or passers-by from pinching his treasure, and went back to the taxi.

'Step on it, big boy! I don't want to miss the plane.'

'Where are you off to?' asked the driver.

'To Moscow, to the capital city.'

He saw Tanya two days later at Khabarovsk airport, when he was already on his way back to Sakhalin, when his travellers' cheques were already spent and he had only a few red banknotes left in his pocket. She was wearing a white fur coat with a belt round her waist. She was laughing and eating sweets out of a bag, and giving them to some other girls who were also laughing. He felt weak at the knees and sat down on his suitcase. He watched Tanya unwrap the sweets like the other girls; he couldn't understand why they were all standing there and laughing, not going anywhere. Then he saw that spring had arrived, that it was a spring night, with the moon over the airfield looking like an orange. It wasn't cold now and you could just stand like this and watch the lights and dream for a moment with a sweet in your mouth . . .

'What's up with you, Kirpichenko?' A friend of his from Sakhalin called Manevich, also on his way back from leave, touched him on the shoulder. 'Come on! They're calling our flight.'

'Manevich, do you know how many miles it is to the moon?' Kirpichenko asked.

'Sounds as if you've been overdoing things a bit while you were away,' said Manevich peevishly and started to walk off.

Kirpichenko grabbed him by the coat tail.

'But you're a specialist, Manevich,' he begged, looking over towards Tanya. 'You *must* know, dammit . . .'

'Well, it's about 186,000,' said Manevich, pulling himself free.

Half-way to the Moon

'Not far,' thought Kirpichenko. 'Nothing to it.' He looked
at Tanya and thought how he would remember her when he
went up that mountain on his tractor, and how he would
forget her at the top—there were too many things to think
of there. He would remember her again later at the end
of the way down. He would remember her all evening
and all night. He would wake up in the morning with
thoughts of her.

Then he got up from his suitcase.

translated by Ronald Hingley

Five Poems

Leaves and Roots

ANDREI VOZNESENSKY

They bore him to no entombment,
They bore him to enthronement.

Greyer than a monument's
Granite, a roan tint
Like its bronze, who living
Had been a locomotive in
Full steam,
       the poet, unkempt,
Found spades more divine
Than any votive lamp.

Thirst parched his lilac . . .
Like a starstream
           sweat
Was steaming from his back,
An oven full of bread.

His house gaped, empty from
Attic down to hall;
No one in the dining-room.
In Russia—not a soul.

The artists depart, hats
Off
   as to church,

For echoing estates,
The oak tree and the birch.

Burgeoning, they vanquish,
Vanish to new beginning
For the plains and planets,
Away from false gilding.

Above, the forests loose
Their leaves, but out of sight
In the soil fivefold roots
Are twisting, tough and tight.

translated by Robert Conquest

Evening on the Building Site

ANDREI VOZNESENSKY

They nag me about 'formalism'.

Experts, what a distance
You are from life! Formalin:
You stink of it, and incense.

They've got their virgin lands, I know,
Where not one pearl of grain can grow . . .

Art's deathly without a spark—
Human rather than divine—
For bulldozermen to mark
In the taiga's trackless zone;

It comes to them raw and salt
To straighten them up at once,
Unshaven like the sun, pelt
Peeling like bark from pines . . .

Half-way to the Moon

For some girl of the Chuvashi,
Brushing a blue tear away,
Brushing it—sweetly, sluttishly,
Brushing it—like a dragonfly,
To clap hands at rowdily . . .

So to me they mean little,
The spearpoints of libel,
And the furious labels.

translated by Robert Conquest

You live at your aunt's

ANDREI VOZNESENSKY

You live at your ballad-studying aunt's.
She sneezes and wears men's underpants.
The damned witch! How we hate her.

We're friends of the barn, like a good bear;
It warms us like hands stuffed in a sweater,
And smells of bee-hives.
                    And in Suzdal it's Easter!
In Suzdal, there's crowds, laughter, rooks.

You whisper of childhood, as we touch cheeks.
That country childhood, where horses and suns
And honeycombs glitter like icons.
And look at your hair, its honey tints . . .

I live in Russia, among snows and saints!

translated by Robert Conquest

146

Five Poems

Dolphins

VICTOR SOSNORA

I don't trust dolphins.
These frolics come from fishfat.
From the fact that puny sprats
Are always in the swim.
Dolphins's blood
is sluggish
in sclerotic veins.
Their *joie de vivre*
comes from the guts and roes of others.
This is the playfulness of gluttons.
I don't trust dolphins one iota,
these gracious leaps,
and giant pearly bodies.
It's a *corps de ballet*.
This snorting
and galumphing is for films,
for painters putting their talents
into handclaps of colours.
Dolphins dote on music, eh?
What's so cute,
after gorging for a week,
about understanding clarinet,
and cutting comic capers?
Taking lodgings in the sea
doesn't make them into fish!
They fly in the air,
but haven't an earthly chance of turning into birds.
Dancing dolphin ballerinas,
brutes with long beaks
and curving cruel teeth.

translated by Max Hayward

147

A Footnote to the Debate about Andrei Rublyov[1]

BORIS SLUTSKY

No, not everything fits into a scheme,
however much you try:
Rublyov, when he took the vows
was scarcely an unbeliever.

He fell on his knees
before the Word—the one
that was in the Beginning.

And what's the point
of trying to turn
his archangels into peasants?

He was saved not by a swineherd
(symbolizing Labour)
but quite simply
                by the Saviour.

So we'll have to give up
yet another atheist in the making;
the spirit of the Dove, you see,
hovered over him
and he was meek
and mild.
No, he didn't wear a jacket
under his monastic habit!

(As for the Lord,
we'll finish him off
without Rublyov.)

translated by Max Hayward

---

[1] *Rublyov*, Famous Russian icon painter (*c.* 1360-1430)

Good Luck, Schoolboy!

BULAT OKUDZHAVA

This isn't an adventure story. It tells how I went to war. How I was lucky and escaped being killed. I really don't know who to thank for that. No one at all, perhaps. So don't worry about me. I'm safe and sound. Some people will be pleased to hear the news, and others, of course, will be sad. But I'm alive. That's all there is to it. You can't please everyone.

A Sloppy Type

In my childhood I used to cry a lot. As a boy I cried less, and in my teens only twice. The first time was one evening just before the war. I said to a girl friend I had then—and I said it with studied indifference:

'In that case it's all over.'

'In that case it's all over,' she agreed with astonishing calm, and promptly walked away. Then I began crying because she was leaving me, and I wiped away the tears with the palm of my hand. The second time I cried was just now: here in the Mozdok Steppes. I'm taking a very important package to the regimental commander. Where the hell can the man be? The sand dunes all look the same. It's night. I've only been at the front two days. But if you fail to carry out your mission, they shoot you. And I'm only eighteen.

Who told me they shoot you? It was Nick Grinchenko, just as I was setting out. He smiled sweetly as he said it.

'Don't give up; if you do, it's the firing squad.'

They'll put me against the wall. But there aren't any walls here. So they'll march me out into the fields . . .

And I wipe away the tears. 'Your son showed cowardice in face of . . .' that's how the announcement will start. Why did they pick on me to deliver the package? What about Nick Grinchenko? He's a tough, smart lad. He would have found his way there all right. By now he'd be sitting in the warm headquarters dug-out. He'd be drinking tea out of a mug. He'd be winking at the girl radio-operators and smiling sweetly at them.

Suppose I tread on a landmine? They'll find me in the morning. The regimental commander will say to the battery commander:

'What was the point of sending an inexperienced soldier, Lieutenant Burakov? You didn't give him a chance to get used to his surroundings. Your negligence has cost us a good man.'

'Your son was killed in action while carrying out an important mission . . .' that's how the announcement would start.

'Hey, where are you going?'

It's me they're shouting at. I see a small trench and someone waving from it. Where the hell do they think I'm going?

'Halt!' shouts someone behind me.

I stop.

'Come here . . .'

I go over. Someone drags me into the trench by the sleeve.

'Where were you going?' they ask grumpily.

I explain.

'Don't you know there are Germans over there? Another thirty yards and . . .'

They explain. It's one of our advance observation points. Then they lead me to a dug-out, which takes a long time to reach. The regimental commander reads the report and keeps glancing at me. I feel small and insignificant. I look at my rather unclassical legs which are spindly and wrapped in puttees. And then at the soldier's sturdy knee-boots. I suppose I must look ridiculous. But no one laughs. Even the pretty radio-operator looks past me. If I'd been wearing knee-boots and a smart officer's greatcoat . . . If only they'd give me some tea. I'd sit at the table made out of a crate and talk to that pretty girl. Obviously, in my present state . . .

'Go back to the battery,' snaps the commander, 'and tell your commanding officer not to send me any more reports of this kind.'

He emphasizes the words 'of this kind'.

'All right,' I reply. And I hear the girl snigger. She looks at me and sniggers.

'How long have you been in the army?' asks the colonel.

'A month.'

'In the army you're supposed to say "Yes, sir" and not "all right", and . . . you've got your toes together and heels apart.'

'A sloppy type,' says someone from a dark corner.

'I know,' I say. And I walk out. I practically run.

Again the steppes. It's snowing, and silent. Sometimes it's impossible to believe this is an advance post at the Front, and that there's danger all round. This time I won't lose my way.

I imagine how ridiculous I must have looked with my feet apart, my hands in my greatcoat pockets and forage-cap pulled down over my ears. And the girl was so pretty . . . They didn't even give me any tea. When Nick Grinchenko talks to officers, he always half grins. Just a bit. He doesn't argue, he just half grins. Then he gives a really smart salute and says 'Yes, sir,' and I hear him say under his breath, 'Go on, give me orders. I know your type.' And he does, too. But my ankle-boots are good and strong. That's a good thing. A heavy, manly foot. It makes the snow crunch. All I need is a fur cap with ear-flaps and I wouldn't look such a misery. Anyway, I'll soon be back. I'll make my report and drink lots of hot tea. I'll have a nap. I have a right to, now.

I've got a sub-machine-gun across my shoulder, two grenades slung on one side of my belt, and a gas-mask on the other. I must look pretty warlike. Somebody once said belligerence was a sign of cowardice. But I'm not a coward, am I? When I was in the third form at school I had a row with Volodka Anilov. I was the first to shout out 'All right, let's fight it out!' and then felt terribly scared. So we went behind the school building. The other boys crowded round. He hit me first on the arm.

'So that's your game?' I cried, and punched him in the shoulder. Then we kept shouting insults at one another, neither of us wanting to be the first to attack.

Suddenly I wanted to laugh and said: 'Listen, I'm going to let you have it in the kisser . . .'

'Just you try,' he said, putting up his fists.

'Or you'll bash me. There'll be blood anyway. What's the difference?'

He suddenly calmed down. We shook hands according to the rules. But we weren't friends again after that.

Am I a coward?

These were the dunes where we stopped yesterday.

'Everyone is here,' said Lieutenant Burakov.

'Where are we?' they asked him.

'It's the advance line.'

Like the rest of us, he was the first time at the Front. That's why he spoke so pompously and proudly.

'Then where are the Germans?'

'The Germans are over there.'

'Over there.' We could see dunes covered with occasional patches of withered scrub. Then it struck me I wasn't the least bit scared. And I was surprised how easily the lieutenant had determined the enemy's position.

War

I've got to know you, war. I've got large welts on the palms of my hands. And a noise in my head. I feel sleepy. Are you trying to make me forget everything I'm used to? Are you trying to teach me to obey unquestioningly? The shouts of the officer—run, do it, bellow 'yessir', get down, crawl, learn to sleep on your feet. The swish of a mortar shell —bury yourself in the ground, dig it up with your nose, with your hands, with your feet, with the whole of your body, not feeling frightened while you do it, not thinking about it. The mess-tin full of barley soup—secrete gastric juices, get ready, stuff yourself full, wipe your spoon clean with grass. If your comrades are killed—dig a grave, cover up with earth, fire mechanically into the air, three times . . .

I've learnt a lot already. Pretending I'm not hungry. Pretending I'm not cold. Pretending I'm not sorry for anyone. I only want to sleep, sleep, sleep . . .

Like an idiot I've lost my spoon. An ordinary spoon. Aluminium. Tarnished, with a jagged edge. Even so, a spoon. A very important tool. I've nothing to eat with. I drink my soup straight from the mess-tin. How about porridge? I've adapted a piece of wood. A splint. I eat my porridge with a splint. Who can I ask for a spoon? Everybody guards his spoon. None of them are idiots. But I have a piece of wood.

Sashka Zolotarev is making notches on a stick. To remind him of the casualties.

Nick Grinchenko's lips curl into a nasty smile.

'Don't fret, Sashka, there'll be enough girls left for all of us.'

Zolotarev is silent. I am silent. The Germans are silent. Today.

Lieutenant Burakov goes about unshaven. It's for show, I'm sure of that. No order to open fire. There's a parley going on. There goes our commanding officer making a round of the mortar crews. Meantime the mortars are in the trenches, in a hollow. And the trenches have been dug in accordance with army regulations. But we don't study the regulations.

Gunner Gavrilov comes over. He sits down. He looks at the cigarette I've rolled. 'What are you smoking your head off like that for?'

'Why?'

'The wind's blowing the sparks about. It's dark outside. They'll be seen,' he says, and looks round.

I stub out the cigarette against the sole of my boot. Sparks fly all over the place like a firework. And all at once a six-barrel mortar on the German side responds. The shell lands with a crump somewhere to the rear of us. And Gavrilov crawls over the snow.

'I ——ing well told you so!' he shouts.

Bang after bang. Bang after bang. Closer and closer . . . My mates run past me to their mortars. While I stay sitting on

the snow . . . It's my fault. How will I ever face them again?
Here comes Lieutenant Burakov. He's shouting something.
And the shells keep raining down.

Then I get up and start running too and shouting:
'Comrade Lieutenant! Comrade Lieutenant!'

The first mortar grunts. It gives you a comforting feeling.
Just as though we'd found strong, cool-headed friends. Then
the shouting dies down. Now all four mortars are firing
somewhere into the sky from the hollow. And only the telephonist, skinny young Gurgenidze, gives a screech of delight.

'A hit! A hit!'

I do what I am supposed to. I drag a box of mortar shells
out of the shelter. How strong I am. And I'm not a bit
afraid. I drag over the boxes. Rumbling, shouting, and an
acrid smell of explosive. Everything's confused. God, what a
fight! A real massacre! Clouds of smoke everywhere. No,
I'm making it all up. Not one shell has been aimed at us.
It's us making all the noise. But I'm the culprit. And everyone knows. And they'll all be waiting for me to tell them
I'm sorry.

It's already getting dark. My back hurts. I can hardly
manage to pick up the snow and swallow it.

'All clear!' shouts Gurgenidze.

I'll tell the battery commander everything. Let them see
I'm not trying to hide anything.

'Comrade Lieutenant.'

He's sitting on the edge of the trench and running his
finger over the map. He looks at me and I understand; he's
waiting for me to own up.

'It's all my fault . . . I just didn't think . . . Do what you
like with me . . .'

'And what am I supposed to do with you?' he asks thoughtfully. 'What have you been up to?'

Is he joking? Or has he forgotten? I tell him everything.
I get it off my chest. He looks at me in astonishment. Then
he shrugs his shoulders.

'Listen. Go and have a rest. What are you talking about,
your cigarette? We merely launched an attack. We had to
start firing. Go on, go away.'

I go away.

'See you don't fall asleep. Or you'll freeze,' he calls after me.

An hour later we're on our feet again. We're firing at the Germans again. Attack. I can't see one. How can it be an attack if we stay in one spot? Is that how it's always going to be? Rumbling, the smell of explosive, Gurgenidze shouting 'It's a hit! It's a hit!' and this wretched hollow, from which you can't see anything. And an attack somewhere or other. Tanks rolling along, infantry, cavalry, people singing the *Internationale*, falling dead without letting go of the colours.

And when there's a brief lull, I run to the observation point. I'll have a look, even if it's only out of the corner of my eye and see what the attack's like. I'll breathe it in. After all, the OP isn't anything special, it's simply a hilltop, and the observers are lying on the side there with their heads slightly raised, and the battery commander Burakov is looking through a stereo-telescope. So I crawl up the steep hillside and raise myself waist-high. And I hear birds singing. Birds!

Someone drags me down by the feet.

'Do you want to get yourself killed?' hisses Burakov. 'What the hell are you doing here?'

'I wanted to have a look,' I answer.

The observers laugh.

'There are birds over there,' I say.

'Birds?' repeated the commander.

'Yes, birds.'

'What birds?' asks telephonist Kuzin from a trench.

'Birds,' I answer, beginning to wonder what it's all about myself.

'Do you really think those are birds?' asks the battery commander wearily.

'Birds indeed!' laughs Kuzin.

I begin to see the point. One of the observers hangs his cap on the end of a stick and raises it in the air. All at once the birds start singing.

'Got it?' asks Burakov.

He's a nice chap. Anyone else would have been livid with fury and cursed like hell. He's a nice fellow is our battery commander. I would have been killed a moment ago but for him. It was probably he who pulled me down by the feet.

It's getting darker and darker. The grey dusk envelops the hill. A long, long way away I can hear a machine-gun firing.

'Machine-gun!' I shout.

No one pays any attention.

'They're ours,' says battery commander Burakov. 'We start any moment.' Then he turns to me and says, 'All right then, have a look.'

I squat down by the telescope and look. I see the steppes. A settlement stretches in a line across the far edge against a background of grey sky. And tracer bullets keep flying in coloured lines from one end of it to the other. Then I hear the rattle of machine-guns and the staccato sound of sub-machine-guns. But I can't see any attack. I can't see any people.

'Come on, come on!' shouts someone behind me.

'Where to?'

And then I suddenly catch sight of something—solitary figures running across the steppes, all hunched up. But only a few of them.

'That's enough,' says the commander. 'Go back to the battery.'

I roll down the hill. I run. And a jeep comes floating towards me, bumping up and down over the hillocks. There's a general sitting inside. I don't know what to do; should I run past or march past saluting as I go . . .

The general is purple. He doesn't see me. He's waving his hands all over the place. And the jeep gets near the observation point. The battery commander is already standing to attention. And the telescope is standing motionless on its three legs too.

And the general jumps out of the jeep and hurries over to the commander.

'You're firing on your own men! Your own men!'

The battery commander is silent. But his head moves from side to side.

Then the general looks through the telescope, and Burakov explains something to him. And the general shakes
him by the hand . . .

Wonders never cease! I think to myself.

'Cease fire!' calls Kuzin into his telephone.

The battery is silent. Just as if everyone were listening
for something. And the mortars are sitting on their haunches
like dogs and not making any noise.

'What's the matter with your hands?' asks the sergeant-
major.

My palms are covered with blood. I can't imagine where
the blood could have come from. I shrug my shoulders.

'It's from the boxes of shells,' says Shongin.

They'll bandage them for me presently.

The sergeant-major turns and leaves. He's probably gone
to fetch the medical orderly. I stand with outstretched hands.
They must have bled a tremendous amount! Someone will
come and bandage them, and I'll write a letter home . . .

'Go and wash your hands,' says the sergeant-major, turning
round. 'We're about to change position.'

The Little Bell is a Gift from Valdai

Help me. Save me. I don't want to die. A small piece of lead
in the heart, or the head, and I've had it. And then my warm
body won't be warm any longer? Let there be suffering. Who
said I was afraid of suffering? It was back at home that I
was afraid of so many things. At home. But now I've got to
know everything, try everything. Isn't that enough for one
person to know? I'm fit to live, aren't I? Help me. Why, it's
ridiculous to kill somebody who hasn't had time to do anything. I didn't even get as far as the fourth form. Help me.
I don't mean with love. To hell with that, with love. I'm
content not to love. Anyway, I already have. If it comes to
that, I've had my fill of love. I've got a mother, what will
happen to her? And you know how nice it feels when your
mother strokes your head. I haven't had time to forget it. I
haven't really been anywhere worth while yet. For instance,
I haven't visited Valdai. And I should see what Valdai looks

157

like. Shouldn't I? Didn't someone write . . . '*And the little bell is a gift from Valdai*? I can't even write down the lines. Help me. I'll go through it all. To the bitter end. I'll shoot at the fascists like a sniper; I'll fight tanks single-handed; I'll go hungry, I'll go without sleep, I'll stand pain . . .

Who am I saying all this to? Who am I asking for help? Perhaps the logs in this dugout? They're not all that pleased about being here either. After all, not too long ago they were pine trees and still rustled their leaves . . . And do you remember the warm railway car as we were leaving for the Front? Yes, of course, I remember. We stood by the coach door and sang some kind of marching song. And we held our heads high. But the troop train was in a siding. Where was it? It was the Kursk Station. They wouldn't let us go home. I only just managed to telephone home. None of the family was there. Only Irina Makarovna, the old woman next door. An old bitch. The way she got on my nerves! She asked me where the troop train was.

'What a pity,' she said hypocritically. 'Your mother won't be able to see you.'

I hung up and went back to my mates. An hour later she suddenly appeared on the platform and pushed a bundle into my hands. And then later on, when we were singing, she stood among a group of women looking on. What is her interest in me? Good-bye, Irina Makarovna! Forgive me. I couldn't have known, could I? I could never understand it. Perhaps you're the person I ought to ask to protect me. Well then, protect me! I don't want to die. I'm telling you straight and I'm not ashamed . . .

The bundle contained some dry biscuits and a quart of sunflower seed oil. And I swore I'd keep one biscuit as a souvenir. I ate it. Does that mean I can't even do a simple thing like that? Wasn't it me who remained in full view when the Heinkel swooped down and everyone jumped into the trenches?

'Take cover quickly!' they shouted at me.

But I didn't. I wandered about, laughing out loud. I just don't want to let everyone see me trembling. If only they'd known how I felt inside! No one must know how scared I am. But can I even tell myself the truth? That's what I mean. I'm my own judge . . . I have the right to be. I'm not like Fedya Lyubimov. Do you remember Fedya Lyubimov? Yes, of course, I remember him. He lives in the same flat as we do. When the war broke out, he used to come into the kitchen in the evening and say: 'Those German swine are pushing forward. We've all got to give a hand. As soon as my arm's better, I'm going to join up.'

'You'll be called up anyway, Fedya,' people used to say.

'That's not the point. Everybody'll be called up eventually. When the country's in danger, you shouldn't wait until you're called up.'

And he used to ask me: 'Do you love your country?'

'Yes,' I replied. I was taught that in the first form at school.

Then one day I bumped into him in the recruiting office. He didn't see me. He was talking to a captain.

'I've brought my exemption certificate, sir,' he was saying.

'What exemption?'

'Reserved occupation. As a specialist I'm exempt from military service. They don't want to release me from the job I'm doing.'

'Then go in there and register. If you're exempt, there's nothing we can do,' said the captain.

If you're exempt, there's nothing we can do. So that's it, Fedya. What kind of reserved occupation was that—working in a watch-repair shop in the Arbat? So off goes Fedya to register. He passed me. He saw me. He stopped, and went red.

'Did you see?' he asked. 'Well, anyway, who wants to die?'

He's probably still exempt. Like a famous engineer or a great actor.

We didn't build this shelter. It's a good one. It was obviously abandoned in a hurry. Someone dropped a photo of a girl over there. It's a picture of a plain-looking girl smiling. Still, someone loved her. Why did he forget to take it with him?

'What about you, Sashka,' I asked. 'Couldn't you get exemption?'

'Who could have arranged that?' said Sashka. 'Very few people manage to get exemption.'

'If you'd given something to the right person,' said Nick Grinchenko, 'you'd have got exempted.'

'Doesn't that cost a lot?' asked Sashka.

'Three thousand roubles or so. You could have sold off some trash or other and got the money that way.'

'Yes, I could've. My desk alone is worth 3,000.'

'Then you could have given them that!'

'Cut it out!' said Sashka, waving his hand in disgust.

'Then why didn't *you* get exempted?' asks Shongin angrily.

'Because I didn't have any money,' laughs Nick.

'You talk too much,' says Shongin.

'And Where Is Your Daughter?'

How well everything's working out. Tomorrow I'll write home. I'm alive. What's left of the battery? Two mortars and not more than thirty men. But I'm alive, and not even scratched. Tomorrow I'll write home.

'Let's knock at the door,' says Sashka Zolotarev.

Night. A tumble-down peasant dwelling. The windows are unlit.

I knock on the shutter. 'Madam, would you be so good as to . . .' No answer. 'Madam, I'm still alive. Oh, if you only knew what it was like!' I knock at the shutter. 'The officer's boots go here, the uniform over there in the wardrobe, the sword goes on the chair . . .' 'I thank you . . . And where is your daughter?'

'Sleep . . . sleep . . . sleep,' says Nick.

I knock at the shutter. 'Grouse? . . . Cheese? . . . Wine? . . .'

'Oh, thank you very much A slice of cold veal and some rum. I'm a soldier, Madam.' I knock at the shutter.

'We'll freeze to death.'

'Let's go on to the next one.'

'Just knock once more.'

I knock on the shutter. Sashka knocks on the shutter. Nick knocks on the shutter.

Good Luck, Schoolboy!

'Here's your room. Good night!' 'Good night, Madam. And where is your daughter?'

'What do you want?'

A woman is standing at the open door. She is all wrapped up.

'We'd like to stay the night here, lady.'

'We're the only ones left alive,' say I.

'How nice for you . . .' says the woman. 'You would have to turn up, wouldn't you.'

'Can we come in?' asks Nick.

'It certainly is cold,' says Sashka.

'We'll only stay overnight and then leave,' I say.

It's cold in the hallway. The room inside is warm. A small lamp is giving off a lot of smoke. Someone is tossing and turning on a bunk over the stove. The room is so small. How are we all going to lie down? The woman takes off her kerchief. She's quite young.

'Lie down there,' she says to Nick, pointing to a corner. A good place for Nick. 'And you come here,' she says to Sashka.

Zolotarev spreads his greatcoat out under the table and lies down on it. And Nick takes off his outer clothing in silence. They put me up on a small bench beneath the stove. There's only room to lie on my side. To hell with it! Who cares as long as you can stretch out. And the woman herself lies down on a bed, a campbed, covered with some rags. She crawls under the rags, without taking off her heavy outer coat.

I spread my greatcoat on the bench. The blue flame of the lamp goes out. A hand strokes my hair.

'Who's that?'

'What does it matter,' says a quiet voice from the stove. 'Crawl over here; it's warm over here.'

'Manya,' says the woman, 'just you watch yourself . . .'

'Who asked you anything?' says Manya from the stove. And her hand keeps stroking my hair.

'Come over here.'

'Wait a moment, I must take my boots off.'

'Come on. What does it matter?'

Supposing we're heard? 'Where's your daughter,

Madam?' Supposing we're heard? There's a daughter for you! It's warm close to Manya. If I touch her, there'll be hell to pay. Manya . . . Is that what she's really called?

'What's your name?'

'Maria Andreyevna.'

For heaven's sake! How can you . . . She has a warm rubbery stomach and small clutching hands.

'How old are you?'

'Sixteen. Why?'

'Sh!'

'Why? Why?'

'They'll hear . . .'

'Let them . . . Move closer.'

'Manya,' says the woman, 'just you behave . . .'

'Mind your own business,' says Manya.

Down below Sashka gives a cough. And Nick says:

'Aren't you cold, lady?'

And Maria entwines herself around me so tightly that I don't know which is her and which is me. We're all mixed up.

'How your heart is thumping,' she laughs right in my ear. 'Are you scared or something?'

And Nick asks: 'Don't you feel cold, missus?'

Is it as simple as that? Is everyone else the same?

'What's the matter with you? Aren't you alive?'

'Let go!'

'I'm only teasing, silly.'

'Let me go, Maria.'

'She's just a silly little fool,' says the woman.

'Let go, or there'll be trouble.'

'Well, let's lie still for a bit, like this. All right?'

'Let go!'

'Then go back to your own bench if you find it so crowded.'

. . . It's cooler on the bench. Sashka gives a cough. Nick says from his corner:

'Lady, you must be freezing under those rags. Do you want me to cover you over with my greatcoat?'

. . . Somebody's walking about. And whispering. It's a hurried, quiet whisper. I can't make out the words. It's probably Maria on the stove over there. Or perhaps it's the woman. Perhaps it isn't whispering, but the sound of silence. But someone's sobbing. It must be hard living in this crowded little place. But tomorrow they'll make fun of me. They will, I know they will . . . And it serves me right. She suggested it herself. She tried to talk me into it. They'll make fun of me. I'll get up early tomorrow and go to another hut, or to the HQ; or wait by the lorries. And she was as warm as toast, that Maria Andreyevna. She'll laugh first. Sixteen! Nick calls girls like that 'peaches and cream'. And who can that be crying? Or is it outside the window?

'Who's that?' I ask.

'Don't shout,' says the woman. 'Go to sleep.'

I must be hearing things. And they'll make fun of me . . . But there *is* someone crying. Or is it Maria crying?

On the Road

We set off for the army base to fetch the mortars. We means Lieutenant Karpov, the sergeant-major, Sashka Zolotarev, and I.

Karpov gets in front with the driver while we take our places in the back of our old one-and-a-half tonner.

And off we go. I'm fed up with sitting around in that idiotic village. Driving about is better. And everyone is sick of it. Sashka and I grin and wink at each other.

The sergeant-major has seated himself near the driver's cabin on a soft seat of empty American sacks. He leans against the cabin with his hands crossed on his stomach and his short legs stretched out, and shuts his eyes.

'We're off, lads,' he says. 'Watch you don't fall out while I'm having a snooze.'

We're on the move.

The lorry moves along easily on account of the slight frost. It speeds from hill to hill. And in front nothing but more hills. And behind us as well. We have forty kilometres to go in all. That's nothing. I'll be able to see how they're getting on behind the lines.

The road is crowded with lorries.

Tanks. Infantry . . . All on their way to the Front.

'The Siberians gave the Germans a licking near Moscow,' says Sashka. 'But for them, heaven knows what would have happened.'

'Siberians are all the same height,' say I. 'Six feet. Specially selected.'

'Idiots,' says the sergeant-major without opening his eyes. 'Height's got nothing to do with it. It was the equipment that decided everything at Moscow, the equipment . . .'

What's the point of arguing, let him say what he likes. I know exactly what happened there. I was told by eye-witnesses. As soon as they heard the Siberians were on the way, the Germans bolted. I know. Because Siberians fight to the death. They're all hunters, bear-trappers. They face death from early childhood. They're used to it. What about us, Sashka and me? Could we do that? Supposing the tanks came right for us, we'd just shut our eyes. And not because we're yellow. It's just that we aren't used to it. Would I be able to go for a tank? No, I wouldn't. It's easier with mortars: you're a long way from the front line. Just fire away and keep changing your position. But face to face . . . It's a good thing we aren't in the infantry.

Suddenly our lorry stops. The road ahead is deserted. Except for a tiny lone soldier a long, long way away, standing and looking at us. The sergeant-major is asleep. Sashka and I jump out. Lieutenant Karpov is asleep in front. His lower lip is drooping like an old man's. The driver has raised the hood.

The tiny soldier comes running towards us. A tiny soldier. He couldn't be any smaller. He runs towards us waving his arms.

'Look, look,' says Sashka, 'here's a Siberian!'

I laugh. The soldier is certainly very small. Then he comes so near that I see it isn't a soldier, but a little girl. She's wearing a greatcoat, neatly belted with a strap, and she has a sergeant-major's insignia on her shoulder-boards. Her face is tiny and her nose just a button.

'Give me a lift, boys, I've been standing about for a whole hour. All the lorries are going up to the Front and there is nothing coming back this way. But I must get a lift.'

Good Luck, Schoolboy!

I help her clamber into the back of the lorry. Sashka and I give her our ground-sheets and she sits down on them.

'Where are you from, boys?'

We nod towards the front line.

'And has the Fifteenth already left?'

Sashka and I exchange glances and shrug our shoulders.

The lorry finally sets off again. The sergeant-major is still asleep. He's even snoring slightly.

'That's wonderful,' says the girl and laughs, 'he's snoring as if he was home in bed.'

'He likes to have a snooze,' says Sashka.

When she laughs, her lips turn up at the corners like a clown's. Sergeant-major! And I'm only a private. But where can this tiny, skinny little girl be from? What's it all about? Everyone's been seized up, carried away, mixed up together. School children crawl through trenches, die of wounds, return home armless, legless . . . A little girl becomes a sergeant-major. What's going on?

'The base was raided by forty Junkers yesterday,' she said. 'It was ghastly. We were dropping on our feet . . .'

'But what would you have done at the Front then?' asks Sashka. 'After all, it's worse there.'

'I suppose I'd have cried,' she says and laughs.

She would have cried, of course. I almost cried, too. Just before the war I saw a film. All the soldiers in it were real men—grown up and seasoned, and knew what they were doing. But I don't know, Sashka doesn't know, and this little girl doesn't know either . . .

'My name's Masha,' she says. 'I'm a sergeant-major in the medical corps. I could beat all the boys in my class at school.'

'And you like to brag a little, don't you, sergeant-major?' says Sashka.

Our own sergeant-major wakes up. He stares at Masha for some moments.

'How did you get in here?' he asks.

'You don't need to use that tone of voice,' says Masha.

The sergeant-major's cap slides on to the back of his head.

'Who do you think you're talking to? It's amazing how ignorant some people are,' she says, turning to us.

I want to laugh. The sergeant-major stares at her for some time and then notices her shoulder-boards.

'I asked you, sergeant-major, where you come from.'

The lorry stops again. The driver raises the hood again. Karpov gets out of the front.

'How are you getting on?' he asks us.

'Your men got frozen stiff in the back while you were having a sleep,' says Masha.

'Oho, what a wonderful passenger!' says Karpov. 'And what about you, aren't you frozen too?'

And he invites her to sit up front.

She skips out of the back and waves good-bye to us.

How nice and warm it must be in front. The air is hot from the engine and the seats are soft. The road stretches in front of you like a ribbon.

Karpov starts climbing up after her.

'No, no, perhaps I should go in the back again,' she says.

'Stay where you are,' says Karpov coldly. And he comes back to us.

'What have you got your legs spread out for, Zolotarev?' he says. 'Can't you sit like a human being?'

We're off again. It's getting dark. If we don't reach the base within half an hour, I'll be frozen stiff. Sashka has wrapped himself up so you can only see his nose, his large, red nose.

'A man needs a bed, not the back of a truck,' he grumbles. 'And a warm stove, and a good meal, and love . . .'

'And who's going to do the work, laddie?' asks the sergeant-major.

When I get home, I'm going to spend all my time studying. I'll always go to bed at 10 o'clock. In winter I'll wear a fur coat and I'll never be cold again. . . .

What a Joke

An armoured car is a very useful vehicle. It looks just like a grey beetle. It can go anywhere and can get out of anywhere. It's nice and warm inside. The electric heater works. You can even sleep as you go.

I am not asleep, just dozing a little. What will happen this evening when we catch up with the battery? Perhaps there'll be fierce fighting. Perhaps we won't find any of them alive. Sashka's sound asleep and Karpov is sitting next to the driver and is either asleep or is just staring at the broken road.

The sergeant-major has brought new boots for us. But suppose I don't get a pair?

'Comrade Lieutenant,' I say, 'if the road had been good, we would have just whizzed along, wouldn't we?'

But Karpov doesn't reply. Must be asleep.

'Fedosyev,' I say to the driver, 'it's nice here inside the car . . .'

'My name's not Fedosyev,' says the driver, 'it's Fedoseyev. You're mixing me up with someone else. People call me Fedoskin and all sorts of other names. But I'm Fedoseyev. Who cares in wartime anyway, Fedoseyev or Fedosyev? There isn't time to bother. Someone once called me Fedish-kin. What a joke. But I'm Fedoseyev. I've been Fedoseyev for forty years. From the day I was born, as they say.'

We are carrying a cask of wine. It's the ration for the whole battery.

'There's a nice smell of wine,' says Fedoseyev.

He has pink, slightly splayed lips, white eyebrows, and his teeth are large with gaps in between. He talks in a sing-song voice. I don't suppose he ever loses his temper. He's the sort who puts you at your ease.

'There's a nice smell of wine,' says Fedoseyev.

The cask is enormous. The hole is plugged with a bung— so firmly it can't be knocked out. Anyway, even if it could be, how would we get at the wine?

There's a bunch of new recruits being checked in at the battery just now. They'll be standing around gaping. What a joke! Just school kids, they'll be. Nick Grinchenko will be strutting about in front of them and showing off. And Shon-gin is probably smoking and saying to Nick, 'You talk too much, Grinchenko!' And the sergeant-major will have brought the boots. Suppose he doesn't give me a pair?

'Fedoseyev, what would happen if you stepped on the gas a bit?' I ask.

'Our speed would be increased,' says Fedoseyev. 'We'd go faster. That's if I stepped on the gas. Only I can't here. The road's too bad. The car will jump all over the place if I do.'

'Let it.'

'What's the point?'

'I'd like to see what it's like.'

'It'd be hard on the car. And people are sleeping. Let them sleep. We're the only ones who aren't. So let them be.'

What if I don't get my boots though? Doesn't he care? You ought to step on it a bit, Fedoseyev. We may still make it.

'There's a nice smell of wine,' says Fedoseyev.

There really is a smell of wine. The cask smells good. And I'm hungry. But we can't drink the wine. It's in the cask, and the bung is the size of a man's fist.

'We can pull out the bung,' says Sashka to me in a whisper. If Karpov hears us, we'll catch it . . .

'Of course you can,' says Karpov without turning his head.

'Just say the word and it'll be out in a second,' says Fedoseyev.

We turn off the road and stop by a solitary pole. We pull out the bung. It's easy. It slides out of the hole as if it was greased. And a whiff of wine comes through the cold air, getting stronger and stronger.

'You can all have a sip of your ration, and no more,' says Karpov.

'Wish I had something to eat with it,' says Sashka.

'We'll get something to eat at the battery,' says Karpov.

Fedoseyev does it very simply. He takes a rubber tube used for siphoning petrol and lowers one end into the cask.

'Hold out your mess-tins,' laughs Sashka, 'so none of it spills.'

The golden wine pours into each mess-tin held up to it. Sashka puts his nose to it. We watch him.

'It stinks of petrol,' he says.

'Doesn't matter,' says Karpov. 'That doesn't matter.'

He takes a few mouthfuls.

'Pure petrol,' he says and spits it out.

'Can't be helped,' says Fedoseyev. 'After all, it's a petrol tube. Wait, let me have a taste.'

We drink up our samples. The wine is strong. You can soon tell that.

'You mustn't breathe while drinking,' says Sashka.

'Petrol fumes are very good for you,' says Fedoseyev. 'They prevent all illnesses. You just have to get used to the smell. It doesn't worry me. Question of habit. Well, come on, give me a mess-tin full.'

'Now give everybody a full ration,' says Karpov.

'How much is the ration?' I ask.

No one can tell me how much the ration is.

'As much as you can drink.'

'Come on, now,' says Karpov. 'None of your tricks.'

I know exactly what will happen. I'll drink it up and a warm feeling will spread all over my body. I shall feel hot, weak, and funny inside.

'Don't you drink too much, Fedoseyev,' says Karpov. 'You have to drive.'

'It's like mineral water,' says Fedoseyev. 'I could drink three pints of this stuff and not bat an eyelid. It's just mineral water.'

'That's right,' says Sashka, 'it's certainly not vodka, mate.'

I can't drink any more. There's a lot left in the mess-tin, but I can't take any more. The skin of my lips has somehow tightened. I can't open my mouth properly. And Sashka's chin is all covered with wine. He drinks almost without stopping for breath. And Karpov clutches hold of the armoured car.

'I'm so weak with hunger, damn it,' he says.

'We've got to go,' says Fedoseyev, and climbs in front.

'A fine place to stop,' says Karpov. 'On this rough ground. You can barely keep upright. There's a better stretch over there.'

'You've had too much,' Sashka says to Karpov.

'I can't drink this stuff. I like plain vodka . . .' says Karpov.

'What's your first name?' asks Sashka.

'Alexei,' says Karpov.

His cheeks are bright red. So are Sashka's. They're like brothers.

We get into the car.

'Do you want some more, Alek?' asks Sashka.

Karpov nods his head. Sashka sucks the tube and wine pours into the mess-tin.

'Here, have another drink.' Sashka pushes the mess-tin at Karpov. 'Have some of this lemonade, Alek.'

Sashka's arms are short, like two tree stumps, and he has a wine cask instead of a head. That's a real head!

'And where are you going to put the bung?' I ask with a laugh. 'Not in your mouth, I hope.'

But Sashka nods his cask-head and says nothing.

'Where's the tube?' asks Fedoseyev.

'In the cask,' says Sashka.

'Having a swim,' I laugh.

'Having a swim?' says Karpov. 'I didn't see it.'

'You're a fine one, Alek,' I say.

He's a good fellow, that Karpov. There was no point in my getting annoyed at him. He now has such a hurt look on his face. I tickle his neck.

'Come on, Alek, buck up.'

Sashka is sleeping with his head against the cask. Let him sleep. He's a good fellow, too. They all are. When I get those boots, I'll show them how to fight.

'Sashka, put the stopper back in the cask. The smell is sickening.'

But Sashka is crying. Big tears run down his cheeks. Like a child.

'Where am I going?' he sobs. 'What the hell do I want to go with you all for? Klava's waiting for me. Klava, where are you? . . .'

What a sickening smell. A mixture of wine and petrol. Supposing you mix perfume and peaches? It's still sickening. What about roses and boot-polish? I wouldn't mind if he just whined away to himself softly, just a tiny bit like a mosquito; then it would be easier.

'What's the matter, kid, do you feel ill?' asks Fedoseyev.

I don't feel ill. Only the smell is sickening. And I can't stretch out my legs. There's no room.

'Come and see me,' says Karpov, 'I'll show you my dog.'

'Where is that?'

'Volga Street, No. 8.'

'What a joke,' says Fedoseyev.

And Sashka is weeping huge tears. He's thinking about his Klava, and wiping away the tears with his hand. I don't feel like crying. Why should I? And Sashka has a cask instead of a head. It whirls round and round. There's nothing you can do.

'They will make you forget me, Klava . . . Buy a packet of cigarettes to give me as a keepsake. We'll say good-bye at the doorway. Klava, buy yourself a bright kerchief . . . and if you come here, I'll give you more money . . .'

But I'm not crying. I'd do better to whimper a bit. You can breathe easier that way. Because this damned smell of wine . . .

'Where are we going?'

'To the battery,' says Fedoseyev. 'There they are, flying through the air.'

'You're not drunk, are you, Fedoseyev? Who's flying through the air? Those are rockets, aren't they? Are you taking us to the Front?'

'That's right. There it is, just over there.'

'What do I want with that, Fedoseyev?'

' . . . there's nothing for me to do there.'

'Let's just drop in for a cup of tea.'

I could do with some tea, too. This damned smell . . .

I open my eyes. The car has stopped. Firing can clearly be heard ahead of us. My head's fuzzy. Sashka's asleep. Karpov's asleep. With his head thrown back and his mouth open. We drank wine. It's sickening.

'Why have we stopped?'

'We've arrived. But the battery isn't here. There's no one here,' says Fedoseyev. 'The Front has moved. We'll have to catch it up . . . But you were in a fine state. Not used to it, eh?'

The car moves off. The headlights are out. Thick snow is falling, making everything look bright. Transparently bright. Like in a dream. I'm dreaming. Or am I still drunk? An offensive is going on, and here we are drunk. I'm seeing things —a figure in white in front of us. It's standing in the road. It's raised its hand. In one hand it has a sub-machine-gun and in the other a masked torch. The yellow light doesn't illuminate anything.

'Stop, Fedoseyev,' I say.

The car stops. Karpov has woken up. He looks at the figure, and reaches for his gun.

'They're ours,' says Fedoseyev. 'Let's find out what's wrong.'

Suppose they're Germans. Where's my gun? It's not there. It must be somewhere under the cask of wine. And the figure is coming nearer and nearer. Fedoseyev flings open the doors.

'Help us, quickly,' shouts the figure. 'Some of our fellows have been killed. We've got to bury them.'

The figure comes up to the car. It's a soldier. He's covered in snow. One side of his greatcoat has been ripped off.

'What were they hit by?' asks Karpov and yawns.

He yawns as though he had just climbed out of bed. He yawns while some of our soldiers lie dead. The man must be drunk.

'Hit by bullets,' I say.

'You keep out of this,' says Karpov. 'Where are the dead?'

The soldier waves the torch.

'Over there. Seven of them,' he says. 'Two of us are alive. Help us.'

'There's fighting going on,' says Karpov. 'We can't afford to be late at the battery.'

'We're late anyway,' says Fedoseyev.

'We shouldn't have drunk the wine,' I say, and am amazed at my own boldness.

But Karpov looks at me and says nothing, because there's nothing for him to say.

'We were all filthy drunk, while there's fighting going on over there,' I say loudly. 'Come on, Fedoseyev.'

We clamber out of the car. So does Karpov. In silence. Then comes Sashka, half asleep. We take spades, a pick, and follow the soldier.

'You've never seen the like of it. There's been nothing like it since the beginning. For six hours we were pounding each other. Then we just went forward.'

We walk across the bumpy snow-covered ground. No, it's

not a dream. The terrible fighting is still going on in the distance. I can hear it clearly. Well, I've certainly distinguished myself. Beneath a low hill a soldier is hacking at the frozen ground by himself. And the one leading us says:

'Here you are, Yegorov, I've brought some men to help. Now we can finish it quickly. Keep hacking at the ground. We'll all help you in a moment.'

A little way away are the bodies of the dead men. They are sprinkled with powdery snow. White greatcoats and white faces. Seven white men lie in silence. How could it be a dream? They're dead. And we were drinking wine.

'A fine commander we've got,' I say to Sashka. 'Drinking like that and letting us drink, too!'

'Shut up,' says Sashka.

'Get hold of your spades,' says Karpov.

'That should go for everyone,' I say with a sneer.

Sashka and Fedoseyev look at me.

'I'm going to dig too,' says Karpov quietly. 'Here's my spade.'

And the seven dead lie motionless as though all this was no business of theirs. We dig in silence, for an hour or two. The ground isn't easy to dig, but we manage. We'll be putting the men in the grave any moment now. Will I be able to look at them?

'Turn out the torch,' says Karpov.

Yegorov puts out the torch. But it doesn't make any difference. It hardly gave out any light, anyway. So why did Karpov go and make him put it out?

The grave is quite deep. The first soldier climbs down into it.

'Right, Yegorov,' he says, and I know what that means. Yegorov makes a sign and we follow him. Do we really have to pick up the dead men in our arms and carry them across to the grave? Sashka and Yegorov take hold of the first one. They begin to carry him. Fedoseyev bends down towards the second. Karpov looks at me. Why should I be afraid of picking him up? I'll pick him up by the feet. It's not his head, after all. I must do it. Yes, me. Not Karpov, but me. I pick up the man by his feet. We carry him.

'Careful,' says the first soldier from the grave, 'don't drop him.'

'It looks like Lenya,' says Yegorov, passing us.

'It's Lenya alright,' says the first soldier. 'Let's have him.'

He takes Lenya's body and carefully lays it down.

Then we bring over another one, and then another.

'Put Saltykov on top. He was a young fellow,' says the first soldier. 'It'll be easier for him to lie like that.'

'Can't you keep quiet?' says Karpov.

'They wouldn't have minded me saying that, Comrade Lieutenant,' says the soldier, 'but I can keep quiet if you want.'

We lay them all in the grave. Neatly. They lie there in their greatcoats. They lie there in their boots. They all have new boots. We work away with our spades in silence. We do everything we should. Everything. And now their boots are hidden under a layer of earth. And a steel helmet is lying on top of the mound. Whose it is I don't know.

We drive off in the same direction. Towards the firing. We don't speak.

Who knows how many times we've changed our position? And how many shells have I passed to Sashka Zolotarev, who loads them in the mortar. How my hands ache. It's not that we only change our position. That would be alright, but the trouble is we keep going forward. Mozdok is somewhere behind us. Come on! Come on! Now I'll certainly get a spoon. I shall have a nice, new spoon. And then as soon as the fighting is over, the sergeant-major will give me those new boots. That's to say, when it's over, but when will it be over? Nick Grinchenko keeps bending down. He crouches down looking through the sights, then stands up straight again. He's quite a tall fellow.

'Platoo-oon!' shouts Karpov. He's waving a branch. He stands there looking so pale. 'Fire!'

Sashka has flung off his greatcoat. The padded jacket has come open. His lips are white. All he does is sling the shells into the barrel of the mortar. Just that. And each time he gives a grunt. And the mortar also grunts.

Through the shouting you can hear the mortars begin snorting in the German positions. And the terrifying shells they fire can be heard bursting somewhere behind our battery.

'I hope they don't get any closer,' says Shongin. He actually shouts it, but you can hardly hear him. 'If they do, we're finished.'

'Retreat!' shouts Karpov.

'Thank God!' laughs Sashka glumly. 'My hands are falling off and I haven't got another pair.'

The lorries come out of their shelter. We hitch on the mortars. Then again we hear the grunting of the German mortars, the whine of the shells overhead and the screech behind us. That one missed. So did that one. How disgusting your own helplessness can be. Am I a rabbit or something? Do I just have to wait until they finish me off? Why is it that nothing depends on me? I stand by myself on a flat piece of ground, and suddenly they get you. It's better in the infantry. Better in the infantry. At least you go into the attack yelling. And then it's man to man; and you're not so scared—you can see the enemy. But here they fire at you and you cross yourself and wonder whether the next one's got your name on it. There it is again. The grunting of the German mortars gets more savage all the time. The shells are coming thick and fast. Our lorries screech like mad as they race out of the line of fire. Hurry up, damn it!

And there's the grunting again. It sounds so peaceful. Again and again. And the whine.

'Get down!'

Back there Shongin is turning round and round.

'What do you think you're doing, gathering mushrooms?' shouts Karpov.

'My puttee . . .'

And he goes on turning round and round like a kitten with a ball of wool.

Something hits me in the side. Is it the end? I hear people running. They're coming to me. No, past me. I'm still alive. Heavens. I'm still alive. I'm alive, alive! There's earth

175

in my mouth, but I'm still alive. They haven't killed *me*.

They all run past me. I get up. I'm unhurt. God! Nothing broken. Shongin is lying a short way away. And Sashka is standing over him. He's holding his chin in his hand and the hand is trembling. It's not Shongin lying there, it's the remains of his greatcoat. But where's Shongin then? I don't understand at all. There's his mess-tin, his gun . . . his spoon! . . . I'd better not look. I'd better not look.

'Direct hit,' says someone.

Nick takes me by the shoulder. Leads me away. And I go with him.

'Spit out the earth,' he says. 'Or you'll choke. We go across to the lorries. They are already moving off. Several people stay with Shongin.

'Come on, come on,' says Nick as he sits me down.

'Everyone all right?' asks Karpov.

'All the rest are,' says Nick.

Towards evening we arrive at a village. And we stop. Is it all over? Are we really going to sleep? Here comes the field kitchen. I've an empty feeling in my stomach, but I'm not hungry.

The three of us sit on a log. I sip my soup straight from the mess-tin.

'The Germans are putting up a fight,' says Sashka.

'Things are really hotting up,' says Nick.

'Our boys have started flying in the daytime now,' I say.

'How's your head, is it still there?' asks Nick.

'He has a head like a mess-tin. It can stand anything,' says Sashka. He laughs quietly to himself.

'I'm sorry about Shongin,' I say.

We finish up our soup in silence.

'It's easier for you without a spoon,' says Nick. 'A couple of mouthfuls and the soup's finished. But with a spoon you spill half of it gettting it into your mouth.'

'I saw some German spoons lying about here,' says Sashka. I should have brought you some.'

And he gets up and goes off to look for the spoons. So I'll have a spoon. A German one, it's true. But what's the difference. I've gone so long without one! So now I'll have a spoon at last!

The spoons are real good ones. Aluminium. A whole bunch of them.

'They've been washed. The Germans like cleanliness. Take any one you like.'

The spoons are in my hand.

'They've been washed,' says Sashka.

A lot of spoons. Take any one you like. After meals you have to lick it clean and stuff it deep down in your pocket. But it's also been licked by a German. He probably had thick, moist lips. And while he was licking it, his eyes bulged . . .

'They've been washed,' says Sashka.

And then he sticks it in the top of his boot. His leggings inside are soaked with sweat. Then he dips it in the porridge again, and licks it once more . . . One spoon has a speck of dried food sticking to it.

'What's the matter with you?' says Nick.

I give the spoons back to Zolotarev. I can't possibly eat with them. I don't know why.

We sit and smoke.

'That Heinkel is having a fine old time,' says Nick, and looks up in the air.

A German reconnaissance plane is cruising past overhead. Our gunners are taking pot-shots at it. But it's too high; and it's already getting dark. It fires in our direction from time to time. You can just hear the rat-tat-tat.

'He's angry!' says Nick. 'I bet that very same fascist was walking up and down this street only yesterday.'

And Sashka hurls away the spoons one by one. Draws back his arm and lets fly. Suddenly one of the spoons hits me in the leg. How that happened I can't imagine.

'Ouch, that hurt,' I say, 'what are you throwing spoons about for?'

'I'm not aiming at you,' says Sashka.

But my leg hurts more and more. I try to stand up but my left leg won't straighten.

'What's up?' says Nick.

'I can't straighten my leg for some reason,' I say. 'It hurts like hell.'

He examines the leg.

'Take down your trousers a moment,' he orders.

For God's sake! What for? I'm not wounded, not even scratched . . . But I feel horribly scared. I have a strange sick feeling, inside, somewhere near my heart.

'Take your trousers down, you bastard!'

I let down my trousers. My left hip is a mass of blood. There's a small black hole in the leg of my white underpants; the blood is coming from there . . . blood . . . But the pain has eased . . . it's just that I feel dizzy. And slightly sick.

'The spoon couldn't have done that, could it?' says Sashka in alarm. 'What can have happened?'

'It was the Heinkel,' says Nick. 'You're lucky you didn't catch it in the head.'

I've been wounded! How could that have happened? No fighting, nothing. In the still of the evening. I didn't rush an enemy observation point. I wasn't in a bayonet charge. Nick goes off somewhere, comes back, goes off again. The leg won't go straight.

'It nicked the vein,' says Sashka.

'Why doesn't someone come to help me,' I say. 'I shall bleed to death.'

'Don't worry, you've got plenty of blood left. Lean against this. Lie down for a while.'

Here comes Nick with a medical orderly, who gives me an injection.

'That's so you won't get tetanus,' he says.

He bandages me up. They lay me on someone's greatcoat. Someone comes and goes. Nothing seems to matter any more. I lie there for a long time. I don't feel the cold. I hear Nick shouting:

'The man will freeze! He ought to be sent to the dressing station, but that damn sergeant-major won't give us a truck.'

Who's he talking to? Aha, the battery commander is coming over to me. He says nothing. He looks at me. Should I ask him to let me have those boots? Anyway, what use would they be now? A big lorry is driving up. It's carrying empty steel petrol drums.

178

Good Luck, Schoolboy!

'We'll have to put him between the drums,' I hear the battery commander say.

Who cares where they put me.

Someone stuffs some papers in my pocket. I can't make out who it is. Who cares anyway?

'They're your papers,' says Sashka. 'Hand them over at the dressing station.'

They put me in the back of the truck. The empty drums stand round me like sentries.

'Good-bye,' says Nick. 'It's not very far.'

'Good-bye, Nick.'

'Good-bye,' says Sashka Zolotarev. 'See you soon.'

'Good-bye,' I say, 'of course, you will.'

And the lorry drives off. I sleep while we drive back down the road by which we've been moving north. I feel warm and snug. The drums are all round me.

I wake up for a few minutes when they carry me into the dressing station hut. They put me down on the floor. And I fall asleep again.

. . . It's a large, fine room. With panes in the windows. And warm. There's a stove. Someone keeps pulling at me. It's a nurse in a white overall over her jackets.

'Let's have your papers, dear,' she says. 'You have to be checked in for the hospital train. They're sending you to the rear!'

I take the papers out of my pocket, and out comes a spoon as well. A spoon?

'Don't lose your spoon,' says the nurse.

A spoon? Where did it come from? I hold it up to my eyes. An old worn aluminium spoon, with the name Shongin scratched on the handle. When could I have got hold of it? Shongin . . . Shongin . . . Something to remember you by. Nothing is left except the spoon. Only the spoon. Think of the wars he went through, but this was his last. There always had to be a last one. And his wife doesn't know about it. Only I know. I'll hide away the spoon. I'll always have it with me. I'm sorry, Shongin, old soldier.

The nurse gives me back my papers.

'Go to sleep,' she says. 'Why are your lips trembling? You don't need to be scared now.'

I'm not scared now. What does 'now' mean? Now I don't want anything at all. Not even those boots. Now I'm completely alone. Suppose Nick suddenly came in and said, 'We're going into the attack. Now we'll have some fun, mates. When it's all over there'll be brandy all round.' Or if Sashka Zolotarev came in and said, 'My hands are just dropping off and I haven't got another pair.' Or if Shongin said, 'You talk too much. You're all bastards!' But Shongin won't say anything any more. Nothing. A hell of a soldier *I* am! I haven't even once fired my gun. I haven't even seen one live German. A hell of a soldier I am! I haven't got a single medal . . . But there are other soldiers lying beside me. I hear them groaning. They're real soldiers. They've been through everything. They've seen everything.

Some new casualties are brought into the hut. One is put down next to me. He looks at me. The bandage has slipped off his forehead. He pushes it back into place. He swears.

'Be with you in a moment, dear,' says the nurse.

'I'm sick enough without you,' he says to her. And he looks at me. He has big, vicious eyes.

'You from the mortar battery?' he asks.

'Yes,' I say. 'Do I know you? Do you know our men?'

'Yes, I know them,' he says. 'I know them all.'

'When did you get it?'

'This morning. Just now. When do you think?'

'What about Nick Grinchenko?'

'Yes, and your Nick.'

'And Sashka, too?'

'Yes, and Sashka. The lot of them. Wiped clean out. I'm the only one left.'

'And the battery commander?'

He begins shouting at me:

'I told you, the lot of them! The lot of them!'

And I shout back:

'You're lying. It's all lies!'

'He doesn't know what he's talking about,' says someone. 'Can't you see his eyes?'

'Don't listen to him,' says the nurse. 'He's not in his right mind.'

'He talks too much,' I say. 'Our boys are advancing.'

Good Luck, Schoolboy!

And I want to cry. Not because of what he said. But because you can cry for other reasons than grief. Cry on, cry on . . . Your wound isn't that bad, schoolboy. You've got a long way to go. You'll still be around for a while.

translated by John Richardson

The Chase

YURI NAGIBIN

'WE'RE NOT taking any more,' said the manager of the game preserve. He was standing on the steps of the unfinished raw-timbered porch. His pallid blue gaze tailed off somewhere in the distance above the head of the man he was talking to.

'Acts like a general,' thought Anatoli, surveying from below the short, stocky figure in its dark quilted jacket drawn in tightly with a broad officer's belt.

'Then take them for free,' said Anatoli, shifting to a firmer grip on his crutches.

The ducks began to scuffle about in the basket slung over his shoulder. He banged on the lid with the palm of his hand and they calmed down. The pale-blue eyes turned slowly towards him.

'Free?' repeated the manager. 'Fancy yourself as a guide then?'

Anatoli flushed. He had no doubt that, as the best gun in Podsvyatye and a former game warden, he would be offered a job at the newly created preserve, and ducks had nothing to do with it.

When the Great Lake was declared a preserve he was delighted. In spite of all the efforts of the local people, poaching had never been stopped altogether and each spring and early autumn, before the season opened, you could always hear the crackle of unlawful shots across the Great Lake. It was not of course like the wholesale slaughter of the years after the war but, all the same, year after year the lake was being robbed of its wildfowl. And then at last Moscow had remembered the Great Lake and taken it in hand.

Pines were felled on the steep bank of Dunyashkin Creek,

clearing a site for a shooting lodge, offices, etc. It was announced in the villages that they were buying duck and geese at high prices to be let out on the lake. They came of wild stock; basically lean and tough, they could easily shed their extra fat and learn to fly. Convinced that he would be hired to work as a guide on the preserve, Anatoli had hurried to finish his work at home—to re-timber the roof, to build a sty for the hog, only, he now saw, to arrive too late with his duck. Of course he had hoped to be paid for them but if not, it was just too bad—he was not going to cart them home again. But Burenkov had mistaken his intentions. And it was not so much being suspected of a mercenary motive which embarrassed Anatoli; Burenkov seemed to be making no move to give him a job. That was why he flushed, all over his pale, freckled face and neck, down the triangle of chest left bare by his open shirt.

This only confirmed Burenkov's belief in his own shrewdness. Stolid and mediocre yet greedy for material gain, he always suspected self-interest in others and saw in this his own strength. He saw all other human motives in terms of camouflage, deceit and hypocrisy. What was more, he instinctively disliked the man standing before him now. Had he made the effort to formulate the vague shape of his hostility it would have come out something like this: 'I have heard that you are the canniest hunter and the best keeper around here and I don't like that to begin with. I don't like the best. You lost a leg in the war. That's a big blow, it handicaps a man a lot, but not you. You paid no attention. You even do better than people with two legs. And that makes you one of those restless types who always have to do the impossible. I don't like you. And perhaps the stories that go around are exaggerated. People always make allowances for beggars and cripples.' This last defensive thought became the basis for his relations with Anatoli.

'Can you do any carpentry?' he asked.

'Any man from Podsvyatye can,' replied Anatoli.

'I'm asking *you*,' said Burenkov, looking at the strong hands gripping the crutch handles.

'Sure I can.' Anatoli took his hands off his crutches, resting on his armpits.

'Don't you "sure" me! Did you answer your commanding officer like that in the army?'

'I can, *sir!*' Anatoli barked inanely, his upper lip curled in momentary scorn.

Burenkov heard the words but not the intonation.

'Go to Vasilyev—he can put you in the building squad. Say I said so.'

'And what about the duck?'

Burenkov did not answer. He turned away and, thrusting his hand in the front of his jacket, he went up the steps of the porch into the empty frame of the building—into nowhere.

That conversation was in April, and by mid-August, by the opening of the summer season, most of the work had been finished. On the steep bank above Dunyashkin Creek an entire hunter's camp had grown up, a lodge for the visitors with two enclosed terraces, and a kitchen, an office, quarters for the keepers and the staff, a storage shed, a neat little house for Burenkov and lots of latrines looking just like nesting boxes. Wooden steps ran down the slope to the jetty where a dozen or so motor and rowing boats were stacked. The reed islands on the lake had been equipped with blinds made of birch branches, and circular platforms complete with seats had been set up. The whole lake was staked out with slender birch poles, showing the motor boats the channels free from weeds. Similar stakes also marked the limits of the forbidden zone, the sanctuary.

Burenkov often did stupid things. He decided against the local hollowed-out boat and ordered keeled rowing boats. These were smart and roomy but unsuited to local conditions: they dragged on the silted bottom and the oars tangled in the duckweed. As guides he took on, with rare exceptions, all kinds of rabble looking for easy money. Shooting was not an affair of the heart for them; they were attracted by the tips and the chance to pot billiard balls all day long on the terrace.

Anatoli worked in the building squad throughout the spring and summer, helping to put up the huts and stake out the lake, and stuffing birds for the lounge of the shooting lodge. These stuffed birds were particularly fine: drakes in their spring breeding finery, capercailsie and black grouse in mating plumage, bittern, heron and various kinds of snipe. But for all that Burenkov did not make him a guide. To his deputy, a former Klepikovo warden who tried to put in a word for Anatoli, he said briefly:

'He can't cope.'

'Try him.'

'No point. A one-legged warden—I ask you! We'd be the laughing stock of Moscow.'

It was as if he even believed it himself now. Out of the whole complex of his hostile feelings towards Anatoli he now retained only one idea: his uselessness.

In mid-August the season opened. Each Saturday buses, trucks and cars arrived from Moscow. The visitors changed quickly into their quilted jackets, waterproof capes and dungarees, got into the motor boats and set off with the guides over the Great Lake. Some of the sportsmen stayed at Dunyashkin Creek where there was quite good shooting too, especially on the wing.

Burenkov himself supervised their departure. This was his big moment. Standing on the steps he would shout to the guides, telling them where they had to go. He obviously pictured himself as a leader in battle. His commands seemed pointless to Anatoli. Burenkov knew neither the lakes nor the birds' habits; he did not understand the sportsmen and what each one needed. He would send a novice to Dunyash-kin Creek where the game was scarce and an old hand to Berezovy Kor, where there was plenty of game but where you couldn't get a bird in flight because of trees and bushes in the line of fire. He gave the best places to beginners who would only waste powder and made the real experts go to places where the shooting was poor.

Once Anatoli tried to interfere.

'And what are you doing here?' asked Burenkov, his eyes lazily lowered, not even looking at him. 'Have they paid you off?'

'Yes.'

'Well beat it—go off home to your missus.'

But Anatoli was a proud man who knew his own worth and he didn't go home. His whole life was bound up with shooting and the lake. From the age of nine he had never been parted from his gun, except to change it for a rifle in the war. After being seriously wounded in the very first battle he had come straight back from hospital to Podsvyatye.

Though the stump of his leg was still alive with pain he cleaned his old gun and went off to the Great Lake for a fortnight. Life was nothing for him without shooting. He only slept well in a canoe. All his important and serious thoughts came to him on the lake and he even composed poems there. Like all good sportsmen he was not out for gain. He always shot sparingly, and only on the wing. He never allowed the excitement to get the better of the sport's inherent discipline. His shooting was like a part of that natural life cycle in which a predetermined number of animals, birds and fish die each year to balance the forces of nature.

With the passing years he became more and more drawn to the role of guide. He was pleased when a novice had his first success, when over-confident owners of Sauers and hand-made Tulkas showed their lack of skill and then, on becoming his obedient pupils, acquired sound habits, and when the rare real masters came to the places chosen for them, filled their bags full and with a silent good-natured smile acknowledged his part in their success. He liked all these people and worked enthusiastically for them. Many of them became his regular clients and no one had ever deserted one-legged Anatoli for any other guide. And now that man had appeared, the all-powerful lord of the Great Lake, and without even trying him out, had denied him his one passion in life.

The carpenters' work on the base was nearly done but Anatoli would still come every Friday, as if reporting for duty, and only left on Tuesdays when the last visitors went home. He still hoped that something would happen to force Burenkov to seek his services, so he came to the base in full kit with two live decoys in his basket, a haversack, stuffed birds, a Thermos brimful of strong sweet tea, a full cartridge belt and a torch.

In his raucous voice Burenkov called out the names of the keepers and gave them their routes. Anatoli stood erect by the jetty leaning lightly on his crutches, his back slightly arched, in full kit, and waited for a miracle. He did not know how to beg, and what good was it anyway? The jetty emptied, the noise of the motor boats died away in the distance . . . and Burenkov went past Anatoli up into the lodge to drink tea from the samovar.

On one occasion a particularly large number of sportsmen had arrived and the keepers had a hard time getting them all out to the blinds. Dawn was drawing near and people were beginning to grumble on the jetty. They were afraid they were going to miss the hunter's golden hour. Two or three rowing boats were rocking by the jetty but there was no one to take the oars. Anatoli swung his crutches and lightly propelled himself towards Burenkov.

'I'll go.'

If he had said it ingratiatingly, with any hint of a request, Burenkov would have given way—but the firm, calm, assertive voice irritated him.

'And what good are you? You'd only cause no end of trouble.'

'I've gone often enough in my time and nobody has ever complained.'

'And what if there was a poacher?' Burenkov started to argue, trying to drown out the curses of the people on the jetty.

'I'd take his gun away.'

'When you'd caught up with him.'

'And why shouldn't I?'

'It's one thing on water—but what about on land? Will you chase him on crutches?"

'What's all this about poachers anyway? People have more sense . . .'

'All right now, that's enough talking.'

But that morning, at long last, Anatoli got his break.

Burenkov had slipped away from the visitors and was already seated by the samovar in the lounge with its stuffed birds on the wall when a jeep drove up with two generals. They were dressed ready for shooting in waders, with hooded capes drawn up over their forage caps, and they had no time for Burenkov's excuses.

'We're not here to pay for your inefficiency. It's your duty to provide a guide.'

The solitary figure of Anatoli hovered between two slender pines by the steps, his bag over his shoulder and his basket at his side.

'There is one guide,' Burenkov said hesitatingly, 'only he's . . .'

'Dead drunk?'

'No, a war cripple. He's only got one leg.'

'That doesn't matter if he has a head on his shoulders.'

With unusual haste Burenkov ran down from the porch and hailed Anatoli.

'Take the generals,' he said, meaningfully and darkly—'just make sure that everything's done properly.'

'What's there to watch? Are generals different from everybody else?' Anatoli shrugged, concealing his pleasure.

The generals came up and shook hands.

'Do you know the good places?'

'We'll find them all right. How do you like them—on the ground, or on the wing?'

'The wing for him,' said the older and shorter of the two, 'but my eyesight is a bit poor.'

'Take the generals to Berezovy Kor,' said Burenkov in a voice of wisdom and experience.

'Why there? Why Berezovy? It's better on Maliye Pozhanki,' Anatoli retorted without looking at Burenkov. 'Let's go.'

They filed down the steps to the jetty. Anatoli went past the trim rowing boats to his own rough boat and undid the chain

'Wouldn't we be a bit happier in those?' remarked the younger general.

'In these parts my kind of boat is handier,' answered the guide.

Hopping easily on his one leg he put in the basket, the bag, gun and crutches.

'What's your name?' asked the older one.

'Anatoli Ivanovich—what's yours?'

'Sergei Petrovich, and this is Nikolai Makarych.'

Anatoli rested his hands on the side of the boat and hopped in, making his way to the stern. The generals settled themselves with a rustling of capes on the narrow wooden seats across the boat. Pushing with the paddle against the firm bottom, Anatoli punted the canoe along the shallows by the creek.

'Did you lose your leg in the war?' asked General Sergei Petrovich.

'Yeah.'

'Any medals?'

'A "Soldier's Glory", third class!'

'Good enough.'

The younger general pulled a cigarette case from his pocket, snapped it open and offered it to Anatoli who carefully took a cigarette in his weathered hand, revealing a large swelling on the first joint of his middle finger.

'What have you got there?' asked General Nikolai Makarych, obviously an observant and inquisitive man.

'I caught it on the bolt of my gun.'

Shielding the flame with his hand the general gave him a light from a slim polished lighter. Anatoli inhaled with pleasure. Here at last he was in his element: the lake, the boat cutting the dark silent water, congenial conversation, the respect of strangers whose luck depended on him. They had never even heard of him until today, but now perhaps they would remember him back in Moscow, and if they came again, surely they would ask for him to take them out.

They moved away from the shallows. The paddle sank deep in the soft mud. Anatoli rinsed the blade and began thrusting with strong short strokes. He saw the young general closely observing the odd movement of the paddle in the water. At the end of each stroke, he turned it under the canoe with a kind of braking action. The general saw that the secret of steering was in the use of the paddle to right the boat with each stroke. He gave a satisfied nod and asked no questions.

Anatoli took the boat out of the creek on to the broad waters of the Great Lake. He sat facing the sunrise and saw the great rayless crimson sun trying to break out of the blue-tinted pillow-case drawn tightly over the sky. All at once it rose, and everything under it burst into light—the sweating greyish pines, the mirror of the creek, the dew on the reeds. Each colour ripened in turn: the green of the grass, the yellow of the shooting lodge's resinous timbers and then the red of the rowan berries. The lilac and orange pine trunks were as vivid as a cockerel's feathers.

But farther along the surrounding shore the colours were still dormant. The old elm, half a mile from the camp, was still a dark shape and, beyond, the blue shadows of birches and willow grove melted into something fluid and shifting. And still farther the tall oaks were like petrified smoke and the sky above them was dove-grey now shot through with pale streaks of light. They had to reach their positions before the sun lit up the whole of the shore and the lake. Anatoli bent more urgently to his paddle.

He heard a swish of wings as a flight of duck flew above them and wondered where he might best place the generals. He had several favourite spots unknown to the other keepers. He had even set up his own blinds there and now he congratulated himself on his foresight. These blinds were not far from the camp: if people had known about them they would have been taken already and he would have had to row the generals on to Prudkovsky Creek where there were five guns to every duck.

Anatoli took the boat to a reed island, seemingly no different from any other, velvet dark against the iridescent water. But for him this island was a special one; he was sure there would be plenty of birds there. This quiet place was half-way between the Dunyashkin and Prudkovsky Creeks— the tired duck had good reason to take a breather there.

Moving with his usual precision, he was aware of his skill and rejoiced in it; he scattered a semicircle of decoys and let the live decoy on to the water. The duck immediately tried to make off, soaring into the air, but the horseshoe fastened to its long tether sank to the bottom and the duck splashed heavily on the water. Anatoli took the boat up to the blind, and helped the older general out. He made sure that he had a wide enough field of vision through the birch branches in front of the blind.

'Use number 4 shot,' he advised, 'and at close range, number 5 will do all right.'

He placed the young general about 300 yards away, nearer the open water, where they could count on duck passing

on their way to Dubovoe (a favourite place of theirs, close
to the Great Lake) and also on duck which would fly from
shore to shore as soon as there was any shooting. He gave
the general a scrap of paper with a rough sketch of the area.

'Put crosses where the ducks fall and I'll get them afterwards.'

'Good idea,' said the general, his eyes searching the expanse
of the lake.

'Don't go after any geese,' warned Anatoli. 'You'll be fined.'

'How's that?'

'They're domestic. Let out for breeding. I'll be back soon,'
said Anatoli and pulled away from the blind.

'There's no hurry,' called the general. 'We don't want to
scare the ducks off.'

Quietly dipping the paddle Anatoli went over towards the
sanctuary. Other guides, once they had deposited their clients,
went back to the camp to drink tea and shoot billiards. But
Anatoli did not play billiards and he preferred to drink
lake water with its slightly muddy taste. And also he had
yearned so long for the Great Lake—for its extraordinary
air, for the intense peace which he found only there. Now
that he was once more in these familiar, comforting surroundings he clearly realized how wretched and unhappy life had
been lately.

Even with his family he was no longer his usual kind,
considerate self. Tanya was in her first year at school. They
had just had their first handwriting lesson. 'Daddy!' Tanya
had cried excitedly, 'look what a good circle I've drawn!'
And he had looked at the crooked circle but he couldn't
respond with the tenderness she expected. How strong a man's
bond with his work must be if everything inside him goes
dead once he is deprived of it.

Anatoli glided slowly over the lake which became more
and more drenched with light. Where the sun was rising the
water was aflame; the rest was a milky blue expanse, touched
with pink on every ripple. The distant shores cleared,
roused from sleep and shadow. The oaks were no longer like
smoke; they had become fine great trees. The first yellow
tinge of the birches and the first purpling of the aspen stood
out vividly. In Prudkovsky Creek the shots sounded muffled

and wooden; then he heard one closer by and a swishing noise from the bushes in the middle of the reeds as a flock of starlings which had spent the night by the lake soared upward. Anatoli looked up. A puff of white smoke rose above the blind of the older general. 'Missed,' he thought with annoyance. Then with his second shot the general was lucky. 'And he says he's short-sighted,' Anatoli smiled.

The shots woke the lake from its slumbers. Swallows whirled about almost touching the water. Plump gulls wheeled over the sky and directly overhead a blue hawk flew by slowly. A small green bird stirred in the rushes, and shook a crystal dew drop which flashed sunlight into Anatoli's eyes.

A flock of ducks crossed Berezovy and wheeled towards the sanctuary. Anatoli heard from his left the strong, rhythmic beat of wings. Five ducks flew over, one much lower than the rest; there was something strained and awkward about the way it was flying.

'That's a tame one for sure. Look at his body—all fat. But they soon get used to the wild life.'

The shooting grew louder but Anatoli could still pick out the shots of his own generals. That meant their positions had been well chosen and his first clients of the season would not be disappointed.

There was Saltny Point with its sharp nose, clustered with crooked birches, thrust far into the lake. To his left the stakes marked the limits of the sanctuary. By some quirk of acoustics all the shooting on the Great Lake was somehow muffled and the rare shots from the distant Dubovoe Lake seemed far louder. These short staccato shots only emphasized the silence nearby.

Along the shore by the old Podsvyatye mooring, and to its right towards Kobutskaya Creek, flocks of duck showed dark on the water like rafts. They were there in vast numbers, settled calmly and unafraid on the open water, disdaining the thick grass of the shore. The sight of these duck in what used to be the busiest place on the lake was strangely moving. It was from here that the hunters of Podsvyatye used to set off. They spent the night here in haystacks, lit fires, boiled fish soup, and amused themselves in shooting at a dead hawk tied to a pole. Anatoli had never felt so keenly the change that had come to the Great Lake as now at the sight of this duck retreat. It pleased him that at the height of all the shooting there was on the lake this quiet corner of safety where a gentle brood of ducks could shelter.

The duck of course noticed Anatoli's boat but although they were particularly wary in this season, not one of them moved from its place as if they knew the laws which protected them there. Anatoli had already begun to turn the boat about when, in the very corner of Kobutskaya Creek, a shot crashed out with a noise fearful in this silence. It was lunatic and unreal, but as if trying to assert its reality, its horrible certainty, the shot lingered in a long reverberating echo. Throughout the whole area of the sanctuary wings thrashed as clouds of duck rocketed skywards trying to escape the peace which had betrayed them, and flew into mortal danger. Another shot thundered in Kobutskaya. The poacher was shooting at the flock again. This second shot left Anatoli no choice. He quickly turned the boat and pushed through the reeds to the head of the creek. The boat rustled as it thrust its way through, crackling the dry rushes, but fortunately the wind was offshore. A dead mallard bobbed alongside, like an inflated rubber toy; it must have drifted this way after it was hit. Anatoli thought of the duck shot by the poacher. How many were there still warm as they lay in their fresh red blood? The boat broke through the reeds to the clear water and Anatoli saw him. He had rolled up his trousers and was cautiously entering the water, testing the bottom with a long switch. 'Looks like a stranger,' thought Anatoli, 'No locals would go into the sanctuary. Who wants to lose hunter's rights and pay a thirty rouble fine?' The man raised his switch, beating the water to bring a fallen duck towards him, and then caught sight of the approaching boat. He dashed to the shore, snatched boots, gun and bag, which were lying there, and ran across the marsh to the wood.

'And suppose you meet a poacher?' Anatoli recalled Burenkov's words and his own answer, 'I'll take his gun.' But how on earth could he take a gun from this stranger who was bolting into the wood? Was Burenkov right after all, was he really no good for work on the lake?

The boat was coming near the shore. Anatoli saw among the water lilies the pale belly of a dead teal with its head submerged, then the sprawling wings of a still twitching mallard. He picked up the mallard and battered its head against the side of the boat. The white down of a duck which had been torn apart lay on the undergrowth, its rump and two legs hung on a branch of a shrub. It was a good shot and no mistake. The cardboard cases of spent cartridges bobbed on the water like toy soldiers.

The prow of the boat beached on the sandy shoal. 'Nobody knows I was near Kobutskaya Creek and saw a poacher,' Anatoli thought as he got out of the boat. His mind continued to dwell on this consoling thought while his hands were pulling the boat ashore, reaching for his crutches, attaching wooden slats to them so he could walk more easily on the marsh. He buried the paddle and Thermos in the grass, and threw his rifle over his shoulder, pulling the sling tight. It was not a question now of Burenkov, but of himself. Burenkov could be deceived, but he couldn't deceive himself. It was no longer Burenkov who stood between him and his work on the Great Lake but this man who was disappearing into the wood. With a forward thrust of his crutches, Anatoli took his first step.

The tall rushes hid the poacher but in the dark peaty soil Anatoli saw the prints of bare feet with protuberant big toes. As he looked they filled with purple inky water. What was the poacher's plan? To reach the wood and hide in its depths? He could easily run him to earth there. The wood was eerie and treacherous. The dry carpet of pine needles suddenly gave way to bright emerald glades—one step and you were lost, for dangerous bogs were hidden under the lush green grass. Deep gullies of rushing water cut through the wood. Dark eyes of woodland pools with treacherous marshy edges peered menacingly through the undergrowth. Sometimes, and this was the strangest thing of all, the pools were invisible, hidden under a soft marshy growth—dangerous pitfalls beneath the camouflage of the glade. The village women of Podsvyatye never came here for mushrooms or berries, and few hunters dared to stalk game here. Of course, Anatoli wouldn't let the poacher die.

He'd pull him out and take him back where he belonged.

As he reached the fringe of the wood he saw some freshly trampled grass under a willow and a trail of footprints leading from it along a track which cut into the depths of the wood. They were the tracks of boots—quite new ones judging by the clear imprint of the heels with their small round indentations. The fact that he had put his boots on suited Anatoli. It meant he had lost some time and also that his tracks were clearer.

Anatoli set off along the track. Far in front of him he could see the heel prints with their pattern of rings on the reddish earth and on the hard-packed leaf mould. The poacher had not thought to hide in the wood. Maybe he knew its treachery or he had had time to see his pursuer was on crutches and counted on leaving him behind, or he had some other plan. How long would the chase go on? A few hours or half a day? This track went through the wood, then through bare peat bogs, on through sparse birch and finally came out on to an unsurfaced road still under construction. In one direction it was a dead-end, and in the other it went to the village of Komkovo, where it forked into two branches which both came out on to the Ryazan-Kasimor highway. He had to catch up with the poacher before he reached the fork.

Anatoli sighed. It was about eleven miles to the fork. Even if all went well and he delivered the poacher to the base he couldn't avoid a row with the generals. It was nearly 7 o'clock now and 10 o'clock was the usual time for the morning shoot to end. Who would go and get the generals? Their blinds were on the side away from the routes usually taken by the keepers. They would be worried, poor fellows, until their absence was noticed at the base and a boat sent out to look for them. How badly it was all turning out. But perhaps it would be all right after all. Perhaps he would catch the poacher and still have time to go and get the generals. With this thought Anatoli began to thrust forward with even greater force, his light, lean body swinging between its two supports. Once, as the path straightened, he saw in the distance the dark bag on the poacher's back,

his padded trousers and shiny boots. The bag must have been
pretty heavy for the man to bend his back so much that you
couldn't see his head. 'I'll get him,' Anatoli said to himself.

Breathing was difficult in this wood, full of marsh gases
and the sour, pungent odours of fermenting vegetation rotting in the peat. Anatoli could already feel his heart straining
although he had not gone more than a mile. Surely the man
ahead of him must also be finding it difficult to breathe, as
well as feeling the strain on his heart which was not only
tired but fearful too. Fear was driving him on but it must
also be robbing him of his strength. 'I'll get him.'

The path was crossed by thick knotted roots and Anatoli,
whose eyes were fixed ahead, stumbled over one and crashed
to the ground. People with two legs never fall so heavily and
badly. They have time to throw out a hand, to meet the
earth with their knees or elbows, to arch themselves, to break
their fall. Anatoli couldn't do any of these things. His
hands were busy with his crutches and it was not easy to
pull them out of the sticky earth. He fell flat on his face.
With an effort he sat up and wiped his face with his sleeve,
licked his bleeding lips, and tried to wipe the black slime off
his jacket and shirt but only succeeded in smearing it all
over himself. He picked up his crutches, rose and started off
again.

Now he went along with his eyes on the ground, carefully negotiating the roots and keeping his leg slightly bent at
the knee to give himself more resilience. He was so intent on
looking out for hazards that he failed to notice that the tracks
of the boots had disappeared. He went on a little farther
but there were no traces. Then he turned back. The trail
ended by an aspen on the far side of a long ditch full of rusty
green water. The poacher had got himself over the ditch with
the help of a thick twisted bough which hung above it. He
had then gone into the wood which here stood on firm ground;
it was very dense, cluttered with fallen branches and rotted
pines. There were no dangerous bogs or underground pools
now. The poacher obviously knew the wood and all its
secrets as only a local person could. How was it then that,
from the brief glimpse Anatoli had had of him, he couldn't
connect him with anybody he knew in the area? And to

think of all the times he had recognized people from the villages round about just by their vague outlines in the morning mist or at night! This was something more than keen sight. It was an unaccountable, animal instinct, but just now it was dead.

Anatoli got all set to cross the ditch although he knew how difficult it would be for him in the thick wood, but suddenly he changed his mind. He got a better grip on his crutches and continued along the track. Now certain that the poacher knew the area, he could correctly anticipate his moves. The poacher was bound to return to the track because it led to a rough road which ran for the whole of its length through a treacherous peat bog. So the poacher's escape route was as thin as a thread.

Anatoli's short rest by the aspen was no help; he now felt how tired he really was. His whole body ached, his leg throbbed and his calf felt as if it was gripped in pincers. White blisters had formed on his palms and the blood on his split lip formed into a hard, painful crust. His shirt was drenched in sweat and he had a killing thirst. He scooped the stinking water from a puddle, rinsed his face, neck and chest and soaked his cap. Then he clearly heard the rustle of branches. The poacher was heading through the wood alongside the path, never letting it out of his sight.

Anatoli kept on tripping and falling, but always got up again and pushed on. He had never dreamed it was possible to go at such a speed on crutches. His leg scooped up damp sods of peat and he dragged their heavy weight until they fell off as he struggled to reach the end of the path before the poacher. He was still too far behind. At the end of the path, where it broadened out into the light of the clearing, a figure with a bag on his back emerged from the thicket and ran for the road.

Anatoli reached the edge of the wood and wiped the sweat from his eyes. The bog spread all around, bright green with black scars across the turf. The sun stood high in the cloudy sky; it must have been nearly 11 o'clock. If it hadn't been for this poacher he would now have been collecting the birds shot by the young general from the undergrowth, the rushes and reeds, where the teal, pin-tails and duck, all still warm and heavy would have been widely scattered by the water. He would now have been hearing words of gratitude and he would have been sharing the hunters' pleasure. But the two generals abandoned in their blinds must be using very different language.

If it hadn't been for this poacher he would have been back at base within the hour, having proved to Burenkov that he was fit to be a guide. He would have arranged with the generals to go out again with them in the evening and in the meantime hurried home to tell Shurka about his luck. How good it would be to go into his house, take off his boots in the hall, creep quietly into the clean living-room over the soft white calf-skin rug with its red markings. There he would see Tanya's freckled face bent over her drawing, and little Yura, with his mop of hair, busy making something as usual. He would hear a shout of surprise from Shurka as she came in from the garden. What a full and contented life a man has with his family! What a pity he only knows it when he is torn from them by some evil force. All misfortune and adversity befalls a man outside his family circle, but what can you do? The faces of home cannot take the place of the whole wide world and however warm home may be, you have to go into the cold wind outside.

Now he could see the poacher's back all the time. He could see not only the bag, the padded trousers and the new boots but even the barrel of the gun slung on his shoulder and his coloured cap. But this didn't make things any easier for him. The stretch of road between them never got any shorter. The poacher saw him too. He kept on peering around, and then would increase his speed. Anatoli would also hurry but fatigue would soon force them both to revert to their normal pace—and then it would begin all over again. There was something familiar, painfully familiar in the way the poacher had of peering around and also in his walk; sometimes it was firm and straight, but sometimes he scuttled along. He obviously wanted to escape at any cost. At times Anatoli felt he had followed this man before, that there was already some connexion between them. Either he had actually met him or perhaps poachers in danger have the same manner, a kind of ugly family resemblance.

He had a vague feeling that the man in front was no ordinary poacher. If his only crime was killing a couple of birds in a game sanctuary he wouldn't behave like this. He would try to buy himself off; such people always kept a bottle of liquor or some money in reserve. And then they were already so far from the lake that the man could simply deny the whole thing and say he had never been anywhere near the lake. What sort of proof was there, if there were no witnesses? The fact that his gun still smelled of powder? Well, he could say that he had just been shooting at crows and jays around here. There's nothing against that. In a word, he could easily have lied his way out of it; there was no reason for him to run away. And yet this was just what he was doing as if he was scared to death. And whom was he scared of? Of a cripple without the strength to drag a healthy, strong man back to the camp. Wouldn't it have been simpler for him to settle the business with his fists? All right, not everybody wants to get mixed up in a fight, even with a cripple. Then why not say, 'Stop wasting your time. I'll deny it and you can't prove a thing.'? But for some reason the poacher was scared to come out into the open. Why? Obviously there must be something wrong with this man which made him afraid of people and of the daylight. Anatoli felt that he was tracking some sort of strange animal. This was no simple matter.

A plane roared overhead. Anatoli looked up. It was an old 'corn-cob', a PO-2. The pilot was clearly visible in his leather helmet and goggles. He too could surely see them from above, two tiny figures on a dark strip of road, two travellers who for some reason did not wish to share the dreary monotonous road. It would never occur to him how closely bound these travellers were, or what kind of a struggle was going on between them. If he had known he would have come down as they do when wolves are being exterminated, to help Anatoli capture this two-legged beast of prey. But the pilot knew nothing of all this and flew the plane into the clouds with a droning noise in the air.

The road dropped slightly and Anatoli saw in the distance a tractor rooting out tree stumps. It was from this, not the aeroplane, that the droning noise had come. The tractor tore the stumps from the earth like bad teeth. This tractor driver and his companion who was looping the chain around the stumps—they would also bring him help if he called them. Of course they would help, because right and justice and the law were on his side in this struggle, because he was now in the service of the natural order and goodness of life. That other man stalking ahead of him was the bearer of destruction and evil.

Would everybody really take his side? No, even among honest people there are those who would rather help the pursued than the pursuer—this out of momentary pity, or because they feel unsure that the punishment would really fit the crime instead of being many times too harsh. Seven years for a pound of potatoes lifted from a kolkhoz field had sown doubts in the justice of the law. Clearly, he had to rely on himself in this affair.

His heart was beating up in his throat, his bleeding palms stuck to the wood. He was afraid to relax his grip on the crutches. He no longer felt his leg; it was like a lifeless prop. Now a sparse birch grove came into view. They were getting close to the village near the road which was under construction. The poacher now reached a thicket of hazel trees on the edge of the wood and looked round. He hunched himself even more, ducked his head into his shoulders as if trying to shrink into invisibility and darted into the bushes. Anatoli was struck by the familiarity of this furtive, cowardly, ugly movement. Instantly he remembered.

He and another warden had once followed a long blood-stained trail, dark on the moonlit snow. It was hellish cold, the tree trunks crackled from frost, but they did not give up the search because the steaming trail was so fresh they were sure they would catch him in the act that day. When they came upon a clearing—blue, sparkling and neat as in a children's book—they saw him straightaway, his knife glinting at the throat of an elk he had just shot. They closed in but with the moon at their backs so that he saw their long dark shadows at his feet. He jumped up without a word and, just as now, peered around, ducked his head and darted sideways into the bushes. The warden from Klepikovo shouted 'Stop', and rushed after him. Anatoli, sinking deep in the loose snow fell behind, but he had just caught up when a shot rang out. His friend spun round with a smashed shoulder and hit the snowdrift head first. Anatoli had dragged him back to Podsvyatye; the going was scarcely easier than today.

Sashka, the poacher, was picked up a week later by the militia, somewhere near Kasimov. They took him for a whole day through the woods around Podsvyatye while he showed them the caches where he had hidden all the elk meat. Sashka got eight years and the Klepikovo warden was maimed for life with his right arm useless.

Surely the eight years were not up? Or perhaps he had broken out? Unlikely. He was well dressed with good quality clothes, new boots and a full bag, and a gun. His time had indeed passed quickly if he had taken to his old ways before he even got home. Or had he so longed to shoot that he could not wait another hour? But Sashka was not a true sportsman; he only wanted to kill as many animals and birds as he could. He did not work anywhere, neither at the collective farm nor in the building squad. He lived by plundering nature, killing even nesting hens, game out of season and unwary elk. The urge to kill was the only disinterested feeling he had. Anatoli had never forgotten one occasion. They were returning home together after a good day's shooting. As they came to the outskirts of the village, a nightjar, a good and useful bird, lighted confidently and openly on a near-by elm. It knew its own usefulness and had no fear of people. Sashka, coldly and deliberately, took his gun and the elm spurted feathers, down and pieces of bloody flesh.

'Why do it to one of those?' asked Anatoli.

'What do they matter, anyway?' Sashka replied in a bored, dull voice.

Dedok the old hunter had been there.

'Did you see his eyes?' Dedok asked. 'He'd kill anything —a kitten, a dog, even a . . .' He stopped short of adding 'a man'.

It was true. Sashka let fly at gulls, herons, cranes, bluetits, and stray dogs and cats which happened to walk into his yard, until finally it had come to a man. His years in a prison camp had obviously not cured him of his passion for destruction.

Now that he knew that it was Sashka, Anatoli understood

all his behaviour. Sashka couldn't talk his way out of it. There was only one thing to do: get away. He knew too that Sashka wouldn't dare use force because he had often before felt the iron grip of Anatoli's hand. But he had a gun. Would he raise it again to a man? Is it easier or harder to shed human blood a second time? Better not think about that—better just hurry to that fork in the road and not let the man slip away.

The striped trunks of the birch trees flicked past and the earth became firmer beneath his crutches on the crinkly yellow birch leaves. The path curved again. He could not see Sashka ahead but he could scarcely have gone far. He noticed that the marks of his heels with their rings were no longer so clear, as if he had worn them down, but then he noticed the sharper impression of the toe. Sashka had no longer been walking, but running; maybe he was exhausted, but even so he'd been running.

Anatoli emerged from the birches. Before him lay the surfaced road overgrown with burdock and weed. The left fork stopped short at the river, and the right led to the outskirts of a small village of some ten homesteads, and there it petered out. They had started to build the road in days long since forgotten and for some reason had suddenly stopped. Sashka was not to be seen. That meant he was already beyond the village and on one of the forks leading to the highway. On the road near the village the solitary figure of a woman moved to and fro. She was hauling stones from a heap, packing them into the cracks on the road's surface and beating them in with a sledge hammer. She looked as if she intended to build the road single-handed.

As Anatoli reached her she threw down the hammer and straightened up. She brushed the hair from her face with a gloved hand and stared at him expectantly. She was tall and broad-shouldered, with large hips and firm legs in short rubber boots. Her big build made her round attractive head seem small on the long slender neck. Her full scarlet lips were smiling but her stare was fixed and the dark-brown eyes were hard. But for the boots and gloves she would have been too well dressed for such dirty, heavy work—with her flowered silk blouse, a black satin skirt and a coral necklace.

'Hello,' said Anatoli.

She nodded, resting her hands on her hips and continued to look him over, with the same silent hostile gaze.

'Has a man been this way—short, with a bag?'

The woman was still silent and he added, his hot sweaty face reddening even more, 'He's my friend—we lost each other in the wood.'

'You must like him a lot,' laughed the woman, 'the way you're sweating.'

'Did he come this way or not?' Anatoli said sharply.

'Maybe he did,' answered the woman lazily. 'But he didn't tell me anything about it.'

Anatoli saw that she was lying, that for some reason she wanted to help Sashka. How could he know that this damned dead-end road was to blame? While it was being built the Komkovo collective farm near by had been charged with keeping it in repair. Work on it had long since been abandoned but the obligation remained. And this morning they had sent this woman and she had to peck at this worthless road alone. She had deliberately, from bad-temper, put on her best blouse and skirt; if her beauty and her dress were to go to waste then she might as well make a good job of it! When the hunted man with the pale twisted face had come out from the wood she had instinctively recognized somebody in trouble. He had asked for a drink and she had given him a mug of milk cooled in the spring. He had told her to keep quiet, pushed some money into her hand and had made off quickly towards the fork.

This second one, even though he was on crutches, attracted her much more, with his lean, firm body, the fine manly face with steadfast grey eyes—and he blushed when he lied. But nevertheless, weighed down as she was by senseless heavy work, she identified herself with the hunted rather than the hunter.

'Why don't you say where he went?' Anatoli took a hand from his crutches and wiped his face.

The woman shuddered: his palm was full of blood oozing from the broken blisters. Now she seemed to see him for the first time; his dirty shirt, his split blood-caked lips, his trousers torn at the knee. His behaviour was so calm that at first she hadn't noticed these signs of his ordeal.

'Give us a kiss and perhaps I'll tell you.'

Anatoli was silent. The girl still watched him—he might be sweaty and one-legged but he pleased her even more. He smelt clean and healthy like a fresh strong man after work. And still unsmiling, with her eyes oddly screwed up she repeated insistently, 'Give us a kiss and I'll tell you.'

Anatoli sighed. 'Can't,' he said—'I've got a wife and two children.'

'So that's how it is!' she said with good-natured surprise. 'Do you want him very much?'

'I've been chasing him all the way from the Great Lake— he's a rat.'

'Has he done you some harm?'

'Not just me. He's worse than any wolf.'

The woman believed him. The fugitive with his pale, hatchet face and shifty eyes aroused neither trust nor sympathy. Why should she stand between them? Let them settle it themselves, let them murder each other, if they like. It would liven things up; better than just fooling around with a road that has no start or finish.

'He turned right towards Talitsa,' said the woman.

Anatoli lowered his hands on to his crutches.

'Wait,' the woman held out the crumpled ten-rouble note. 'Give this back to him.'

Anatoli shoved the money in his pocket and started off. The woman looked long after him until he became a tiny speck on the road. Then she took up the hammer and let it fall heavily on the round face of a rock. She lifted it again and with all her strength flung the hammer into a ditch. To hell with it. She would go somewhere where her work made sense.

Anatoli did not doubt that the woman had told the truth, but there was no sign of Sashka for so long he began to worry that he might have turned off into the wood. A shining curtain of rain was advancing, with a loud rustle, from the wood. As it moved, it drew a straight line on the grey cracked edge of the road and now fell upon Anatoli in all its cool freshness. Immediately, he could breathe more easily and his spirits rose. On the other side, the sun, already past its zenith, burned brightly through a blue rift in the grey cloud.

Anatoli noticed wheel ruts and tyre marks on the road. This meant that vehicles and carts passed this way, even if only rarely, and with luck some truck might come along. More cheerful now, he began to believe he would succeed, and indeed before long he saw the familiar figure, bag on back, ahead. Sashka saw him too but he did not go any faster. He sat down on the road and hurriedly put on his boots. He had gone barefoot since the wood. He jumped up and strode on. There was now only a quarter of a mile between them. 'Come on, come on,' Anatoli said to himself, still with the same happy confidence that the chase was nearing its end. It was at this moment that a big truck came out of the wood, pitching over the rough ground across Sashka's path. Sashka waved his arms and the truck slowed down. He leaped up to it and clutched the tail-board; the people inside gave him a hand so he could scramble in. It was not until the truck, splashing through puddles, had raced on that Anatoli realized what had happened.

Anatoli kept on going, not knowing why. The curtain of rain retreated and the smell of the earth was strong. Now and then the vague thought stirred in his mind that the truck might burst a tyre, or get stuck in the mud, or that the bridge across the Talitsa, three miles away, might be down, or that the truck was from the collective farm near by and Sashka would soon have to get off. Anatoli would not admit defeat; he was still not reconciled to it.

'You deaf?' he heard behind him. 'I've been hooting and hooting—didn't you hear me?'

Behind him stood a youth in leather jacket and goggles with a motor-cycle propped on its side.

'I was thinking,' said Anatoli—'Can you give me a lift?'

'Where are you going?'

'To the main road.'

The motor-cyclist righted his machine. Anatoli scrambled awkwardly on to the pillion which was slippery from the rain, found a metal grip under the saddle and held on to it. The motor-cycle coughed, sneezed, back-fired and then, wobbling slowly at first bowled along the rough bumpy road faster and faster. It was hellishly uncomfortable; his leg stump prevented him from distributing his weight evenly and he was in constant danger of being thrown off balance and losing his grip. His crutches were a nuisance as he had to hang on to them as well. But the motor-cyclist, unaware of his passenger's discomfort, pressed on at top speed and they soon saw the back of the truck jolting up and down. The cyclist hooted furiously; he obviously liked people to get out of his way in good time. The truck weaved to the side, slowed almost to a halt and from the back a figure jumped into the ditch, fell, got up and started limping towards the wood. When the motor-cycle drew level with the spot where the man had jumped off Anatoli shouted in the youth's ear.

'Stop!'

The motor-cyclist braked sharply.

'You wanted the highway?'

'This will do, thanks'—Anatoli slid off the seat and without looking round started to cross the ditch. The ground was soft and Anatoli fixed the slats to his crutches again. Sashka was moving slowly. He must have hurt his leg and the sticky soil must be slowing him down too. Anatoli heard the water squelching under his boots and then his hoarse laboured breathing.

On the marshy ground alongside the wood there were some scrawny shrubs and Sashka was trying to reach them as if to hide there. He glanced back and, as their eyes met, Anatoli was surprised by the expression of terror on his face.

'Stop!' cried Anatoli. His own voice seemed strange. 'Stop, I said!'

Sashka seemed to shrivel as if he had been scalded and shot into the bushes. Anatoli understood this movement. He too had had the feeling that he had had some physical effect on Sashka with his voice. Sashka jumped, hoping to reach a dry hummock under the bushes but he missed and sank to above his knees in the soft bog. But Anatoli was also stuck in the peat. With his chest touching the reeds he made a supreme effort and dragged out his leg, thickly plastered with peat, and shoved his crutches forward. He was almost crawling.

Sashka was floundering about in the bog trying to grab the branch of a bush.

'Stop!' repeated Anatoli and drew still closer. The poacher, twisting round awkwardly, dragged his gun from over his shoulder and aimed at Anatoli.

'Don't come near,' he screamed. 'I'll kill you!'

'Now then, take it easy.'

It seemed to Anatoli as if a vast hungry mouth was sucking at his leg. He twisted it in the earth and was slowly drawing it forward when a shot exploded in his face. He felt a rush of air on the crown of his head and smelt the acrid reek of powder. The wad from the cartridge flicked his cheek. 'He's firing wide,' he thought calmly and, finally pulling out his leg, he threw himself forward, almost reaching Sashka. The black hole of the barrel was right at his forehead. 'This is it,' Anatoli had time to think, and the earth reeled before him in all its green and blue as if the earth and sky had changed places. And oddly, in his numb and swooning state, he clearly heard the empty click of the trigger. He had the swift reflexes of a hunter. He swung a crutch and hit Sashka on the hand. Sashka dropped his gun and fell backwards.

Anatoli dragged himself forward and picked up the gun. He removed the firing pin, shoved it in his pocket, and threw the gun back to Sashka. He got himself to a dry place, wiped the clinging slime of peat from his boot and trousers, and remembered that he had not had a smoke all day. He took out a tin box with shag and strips of newspaper, rolled himself a cigarette, and breathed in greedily.

Sashka was weeping and cursing, groveling on the ground in the most revolting way, with his collar bones jutting out from his undershirt. He begged Anatoli to finish him off, even bringing in his old mother, although he had lost her in early childhood. Anatoli listened with curiosity. There was in all this something artificial but at the same time it was serious, like some sort of ritual. Presumably this was how they behaved where Sashka came from.

Then he got sick of it, and, in any case, it was time to start back.

'All right, up you get,' he said prodding him with a crutch.

Sashka fell silent, lumbered to his feet and took up his gun.

'Wipe your face,' said Anatoli. 'That's no way to behave.'

Sashka obediently wiped his face with the back of his hand, then with the lining of his lapels. Anatoli noted this new submissiveness—it was as if Sashka was used to being ordered about and even liked it.

'I was told to give this back to you.' Anatoli held out the crumpled ten-rouble note.

Sashka smirked.

'She's an honest bitch.'

'Shut up. Get moving.'

And slowly, sinking again and again into the bog, they dragged themselves back to the road. Sashka was quiet. Just once he turned to Anatoli and offered to take his gun.

'Let me carry it.'

'No need.'

'Scared?' Sashka showed his uneven white teeth.

'No, it's not loaded.'

'But I've got a belt full of cartridges.'

'They won't do. Mine's a twelve gauge,' Anatoli answered calmly.

Sashka fell silent but soon he became talkative again. He started to question Anatoli about what would happen to him and begged him not to say that he had tried to resist.

'I like that!' Anatoli said with feeling. 'If your gun hadn't misfired I wouldn't be here.'

'But look, I didn't know what I was doing,' Sashka argued hotly. 'I didn't even remember what it was all about, honest, Anatoli. It seemed like I'd lose my freedom again.'

Anatoli felt he was speaking the truth.

'All right, it didn't go off, lucky for you. Anyway you can always deny it.'

'They'll still believe you and not me. I'm in a bad spot. Anyone else might get away with it—but not me, not a hope. I'll get another stretch inside and that's all there is to it.'

'You won't last long anyway at this rate. This was your first day out and you . . .'

'I didn't mean to. How was I to know about the new set-up here?'

208

'Don't be such a damn fool. When did you ever see duck sitting there like that? You could see that nobody shoots them there.'

Sashka gave him a sidelong glance.

'Believe it or not: every night for eight whole years I dreamed I was on the Great Lake and there were so many ducks it was black all over with them. And when I got here this morning that's just how it was. Well, all right, I guessed it was a sanctuary but so what, I thought. I'll have just one more go, I thought. Get it out of my system for good. I'm an unlucky bastard,' he said with sudden bitterness.

This was a very different Sashka. He had far too much to say for himself but there did seem to be something human in him. He aroused pity now rather than hate. If he had not led him such a chase Anatoli would simply have taken his firing-pin and let him go. But he needed more than the firing-pin to deal with Burenkov. Burenkov must have had no end of trouble with the generals and it would need something more weighty than a small piece of a shotgun to convince him—otherwise he would never believe that he had chased a poacher as far as Talitsa Marshes.

As if guessing his thoughts Sashka said:

'I didn't mean to stay here. I've got a trade now—stonemason.'

'They're building a duck farm in Zareche. You could try there.'

'It'd be near the ducks,' laughed Sashka.

Komkovo appeared ahead and Anatoli cut across the open ground to reach the woods, avoiding the road where the woman was working. For some reason he did not want to see her again.

The road lay behind them and they were passing through the wood. The sun was going down, its rays no longer fell straight into the pathway but caught in the bushes and trees. The track was in shadow, cool and smelling even more strongly of sour wine. Once again thick snaky roots lay underfoot, but this time there was no hurry and Anatoli carefully stepped over them. A few hours before he had come along this path in the opposite direction. He had stumbled and fallen. Salt sweat had burned his lips. But he had

felt far better and more sure of himself than now, with
the prospect of facing Burenkov. But when they got to the
lake, where the chase had begun, he felt a stir of pride.
'I made it after all.'

The down of the duck Sashka had killed still blew about
on the undergrowth and the shot-off back and legs still hung
on a branch. With Sashka's help he pushed the dry boat
into the water, put in the gun, the Thermos, the basket
and the bag which had held the decoys. Then he cleaned
his boot and clothes and washed his hands and face. Sashka
followed his example. They climbed into the boat. Anatoli
pushed off with the oar and the boat shot sharply forward.
Some mallard reared noisily from the reeds. Sashka's eyes
shone dangerously.

'You'd better not hang around here,' Anatoli advised.

'Is there any shooting at Zareche?'

'It's allowed in the Por.'

'Duck?'

'A bit, yes . . .'

'That'll do me.'

Silence spread over the lake. Even Prudkovsky Creek had
settled down to wait for the evening shoot. Duck passed high
overhead, singly and in flocks. The ripples were shot with
dark gold; the woods rose green and peaceful above the lake.

'I've been around,' said Sashka, 'but there's no place as
beautiful as this.'

'Pity you didn't notice it earlier.'

'I was just a kid, didn't know what was good for me.'

As they drew nearer to the camp Sashka became uneasy.
Perhaps he was impressed by the big buildings standing
proudly on the slope, the fleet of motor boats at the jetty, the
trucks, buses and cars with their paint and metal glistening
through the pines—all these signs of a big important world
which meant business. His face went white again and his
eyes roved in alarm.

Anatoli took the boat to the shore, threw the chain over
the iron bollard and gathered up his crutches. Pinchukov, the
watchman, was sitting smoking on the jetty.

'You're alive then—not drowned?' he asked Anatoli in
mock surprise.

'Listen Pinchukov, are my generals still here?'

'You might well ask! They've gone, mad as hell they were. They yelled bloody murder. We thought Burenkov would have a stroke.'

Anatoli frowned. Deep down he had counted on the generals. For some reason he had been certain that once they knew what had happened they would have taken his side.

'You'd better not show yourself,' advised Pinchukov. 'The boss is in a wild rage.'

'Oh, well, I'll risk it.'

Anatoli started up the ladder. Sashka slouched along behind, his head bowed. Glasha, the cook-house girl, ran alongside with a swill bucket. She stopped and cocked her head to one side, looking pityingly at Anatoli.

'They'll bury me alive,' he thought to himself.

Burenkov stood on the porch of the lodge, chewing on an empty cigarette holder. He noticed Anatoli, of course, but he didn't move a muscle. When Anatoli drew near and opened his mouth to start giving an account of himself, Burenkov exploded. This sudden switch from apparent calm to wild screaming hysteria was very odd. Anatoli tried to figure out what had happened. He gathered that the generals had not been missed until the chauffeur who had brought them began to get worried, that it had taken some time to find them and that Burenkov had not bothered to find any excuses for Anatoli's absence in any way. Naturally this had enraged the generals. What Burenkov did not tell Anatoli was that on returning to the camp, though they had grumbled, they were more concerned about the disappearance of their guide than by their own troubles. They were grateful to him for the exceptionally successful shooting and insisted that Burenkov should send out a search party, even volunteering to go themselves.

'To look for what?' Burenkov had said. 'He's with his old woman in bed.'

Then there really was hell to pay and Burenkov realized too late that he had made a mistake by doing the dirty on Anatoli. But he consoled himself with the thought that at least he had found a scapegoat and that he himself seemed only indirectly to blame. The enraged generals had not waited for the evening shoot and had gone off in their jeep.

'All right, calm down,' said Anatoli quietly when Burenkov had run out of bad lauguage. 'I've got a poacher here.' He took the firing-pin from his pocket and held it out to Burenkov. Burenkov took it mechanically and looked at Sashka with empty eyes.

'He was shooting in the game sanctuary,' Anatoli concluded. 'I chased him all the way to Talitsa.'

'What do you mean, all the way to Talitsa?' mumbled Burenkov. 'What kind of a story is that?'

Only then did he really see the torn clothing, the haggard face, the blue shadows under the eyes, the cut lips and the bloodstained crutches.

'Ask him.' Anatoli nodded towards Sashka.

But Burenkov did not need confirmation. He already knew this was the truth. If the generals had not already gone, how beautifully the whole affair would have turned out. A cripple on crutches, one of his own staff, chasing a hardened criminal through forest and bog for twelve miles where the going was tough even for an able-bodied man. A real feat of heroism, if ever there was one! But the generals had gone away. And in the report he would have to make, a story like that just wouldn't hold water. People would say he'd made it up. What's more it would only clear the guide and leave a black mark against him for mismanagement. In any case he wouldn't get the sack. After all, he had warned the generals that the guide was unreliable. They were the ones who had insisted. He had taken pity on the disabled war veteran. He had given him a chance to distinguish himself and the man had let him down. A mistake like that even did him credit.

Burenkov had another thought that was quite unavowable; now that the one-legged guide had done such a remarkable thing he had to believe all the good that had been said about him. He was indeed somebody quite extraordinary who couldn't be lightly dismissed. And what was he to do with this wretched poacher? He was some hero too—the column of shit, letting a cripple get the better of him like that.

Tapping the firing-pin on his palm, Burenkov shifted his

stern and penetrating gaze to the small pale man who was standing a little way off. The man gave him a sharp, quick glance in return, his beady eyes glazed over and he started up in a nasty whining voice:

'Don't be too hard on me, sir. I've had eight years in prison, I've paid for what I did. I was a fool, I didn't know what I was doing and I broke the law. If I'd known it was a sanctuary I'd have gone a hundred miles around it.'

Anatoli was silent, watching with disgust the impression Sashka was making on Burenkov.

'You didn't know then?' asked Burenkov.

'Cross my heart, sir. Word of an honourable Soviet citizen.'

'There,' Burenkov handed him the firing-pin. 'But watch out if you get caught again.'

'I won't, don't worry,' answered Sashka with icy calm.

'And as for you,' Burenkov shifted his glance to Anatoli. 'Don't let me see you here again. This is State Property. If anything is missing I'll have you up. Understand?' Burenkov sauntered towards the lodge.

'Well how do you like that, Anatoli?' said Sashka, not gloating too much. Then he suddenly guffawed, 'Quite a fellow, isn't he?'

Anatoli said nothing and went back to his boat . . .

translated by David Alger

Five Poems

EVGENI EVTUSHENKO

Secrets

Adolescent secrets slip away
like mist along the beach . . .
Tonyas, Tanyas—that's what they
were even with their chapped red feet.

So were the stars and animals
and flocks of mushrooms under the aspens,
and all the doors swung secretly—
only the way they do for children.

Then the riddles of the world arose
like little white balls from the mouth
of a fakir in a bewitching pose,
bewitching us to make things out.

Little magic snowflakes tumbled
down on the woods and fields of hay.
Little magic laughter rippled
in the corners of the young girls' eyes.

We whispered something secretly
on the secretive ice of the skating-rink,
and like two secrets, timidly,
we touched our finger-tips.

But suddenly we were all grown-up.
His tailcoat tattered and worn threadbare,
the fakir vanished into somebody's childhood,
like a distant province, to go on tour.

We, being grown-up, were forgotten.
Ah, fakir, you're a no-good man.
The snow now falls down on our shoulders
so obviously it seems a wrong.

Where are you now, little magic balls?
There's nothing secret about our sorrow.
There's nobody secret for us now,
and we have no secrets from the others.

And so, if by chance a hand now touches
yours gently, softly caresses your hand,
it's only a hand—not a secret,
you know this—only a hand!

Give me a secret, a simple secret,
a secret: shyness, silence, things done—
a slim, a skinny, a barefooted secret . . .
Give me a secret—if only one!

translated by F. D. Reeve

A Knock on the Door

'Who's there?'
    'I am old age,
        I've come to you.'
'Later!
    I'm busy now.
        Got things to do!'
'All right, my lad,
            but bear in mind
I'm waiting for you behind this door.'

Half-way to the Moon

I wrote.
    Telephoned.
        Swallowed a fried egg.
Then I opened the door,
        but no one there.
Maybe friends
    were pulling my leg?
Or perhaps
    I hadn't got the name right.
It was not old age had called,
        but maturity.
It couldn't wait,
  and sighing
    departed.

translated by George Reavey

Through the Crowded Streets

Through the crowded streets of the capital
I wander above the stir of April waters,
revoltingly illogical,
unforgivably young.
I take tramcars by storm,
tell someone crazy lies,
and run in my own footsteps,
though I can never catch up.
I'm astounded by the bulging barges,
airplanes,
    my own verse . . .
They have endowed me with riches,
but didn't tell me what to do with them.

translated by George Reavey

Five Poems

Humour

Kings,
> Emperors, and Czars,
sovereigns of all the earth,
have commanded many a parade,
but they could not command
>> humour.
Aesop, the tramp, came visiting
the palaces of illustrious men
sunk in sleek comfort all day,
thought them no better than beggars.
In houses,
> where hypocrites have
left their footsteps,
there Hodja Nasr-ed-Din,

>> with his jokes
upset
> mean minds
>> like a row of pawns!
They tried
> to commission
>> humour—
but humour cannot be bought!
They tried
> to murder humour,
but humour
> thumbed
>> his nose at them!
It's hard
> to fight humour.
They executed him time and again.
His severed head
swayed on the point of a pike.
But as soon as the mummers' pipes
began their jesting tale,
humour defiantly cried:
>> 'I'm back, I'm here!'
and started to foot a dance.

Half-way to the Moon

In an overcoat, threadbare and old,
with downcast face
              and a mask of repentance,
a political criminal,
he,
   now under arrest,
              trudged to his execution.
He appeared to show resignation
as if accepting the life beyond,
but of a sudden
           he slipped out
              of his overcoat,
and, waving his hand,
            did a bolt.
Humour
        was shoved
           into cells,
but much good that did.
Humour went straight through
prison bars and walls of stone.
Coughing, like any man in the ranks,
he marched
        singing a ditty,
rifle in hand upon the Winter Palace.
He's accustomed to frowns,
but they do him no harm;
and at times, with humour,
              humour
looks at himself.
He's eternal.
        Nimble and quick.
He'll pass through anything,
           through everyone.
So—
        glory be to humour.
He—
        is a brave man.

                  translated by George Reavey

The Heirs of Stalin

Mute was the marble.
                Mutely glimmered the glass.
Mute stood the soldiers on guard,
                        bronzed by the breeze.
Thin smoke curled above the coffin.
                    And breath seeped through the chinks
as they bore him out the mausoleum doors.
Slowly the coffin floated,
                   grazing the fixed bayonets.
He also was mute—
             he also!
                   mute and dread.
Grimly clenching
            his embalmed fists,
only pretending to be dead,
                 he spied from inside.
In his memory he wished to engrave
                    each of his pallbearers:
young recruits from Ryazan and Kursk,
that afterwards in some way
                he might find enough strength for a sortie,
rise from the grave,
              and reach out to these unreasoning youths.
He was scheming something,
                had merely dozed off to rest.
And I, addressing our Government, petition them to double,
      and triple the soldiers on guard by this slab,
lest Stalin rise again
                  and, with Stalin,
                           the past.
I don't refer to the past, so holy and glorious,
of Turksib,
         and Magnitka,
                 and the flag hoisted over Berlin.
By the past, in this case,
              I've in mind the neglect

of the good of the people,
                    false accusations,
                                        the arrest of innocent men.
We sowed our crops honestly.
Honestly we smelted metal,
and honestly we marched,
                    falling into the ranks.
But he feared us.
                    Believing in the great goal,
he judged any odious means
                                good enough to that great end.
He was far-sighted.
                    Skilled in the art of political strife,
he left many heirs
                    here on the globe.
I fancy
        a telephone installed in that coffin:
Stalin gives directions
                    to Enver Hoxha.
Where else from that coffin does the cable lead!
No, Stalin has not given in.
                                He thinks he can
                                                outwit death.
We bore him out of the mausoleum.
But how, out of Stalin, shall we bear
                                Stalin's heirs!
Some of his heirs trim roses in retirement
secretly thinking
                    their discharge is temporary.
Others,
        from rostrums, even heap abuse on Stalin
but,
    at night,
            hanker after the good old days.
No wonder Stalin's heirs seem stricken
with heart attacks these days.
                    They, once the stalwarts,
detest this time
                    of empty prison camps

Five Poems

and halls packed with people listening

                to poets.

The Party forbids me

          to be smug.

'Why bother?'

             some urge me—but I can't be quiet.

While the heirs of Stalin walk this earth,

Stalin,

     I fancy, still lurks in the mausoleum.

translated by George Reavey

On Both Sides of the Ocean

VICTOR NEKRASOV

In Italy

IT WAS on my previous visit to Italy, at the Vatican, that I first saw throngs of tourists (mostly West Germans) filling page after page of their notebooks, although everything the guides were telling them was already in the guidebooks they held gripped under their arms. It was then that I conceived a dislike for notebooks. In America this dislike was reinforced when I noticed some of our own tourists doing the same thing—writing constantly, without finding time to glance at the paintings in front of them . . .

A writer, in my view, needs a notebook chiefly to record phone numbers and addresses—for the rest, it only gets in the way . . .

Yes, I am definitely against notebooks and against the planning of 'tours and visits', against schedules. The most interesting things turn up suddenly, when least expected, though this element of unexpectedness has its reefs and rapids.

To lead off, let me relate an incident that occurred not in Italy, it is true, but here in the Soviet Union; it involved an Italian, however. It still gives me the shivers just to recall this incident.

This Italian—Giulio Einaudi—is a prominent publisher in Turin, the son of a former President, and a friend of the Soviet Union who has done a great deal to popularize Soviet literature in Italy. He had come not by himself but with his wife and a friend, the Venetian writer Quarantotti Gambini.

They stayed in Kiev two or three days. They drove around town, took in the sights; it was all as it should be, as custom dictates. But suddenly out of the blue Einaudi had a desire to go to the market. It should be pointed out that in general foreigners like to visit the markets, but, more than that, someone had told our Einaudi that only at the market were genuine works of folk art to be had. As it later turned out, the reference was to the swans daubed on oilcloth and the striped goggle-eyed papier-mâché cats, nothing more. Well, let it be the market, then. We got into the Intourist car and off we went to the Zhitny Market in the Podol quarter. Besides the guests there was a young woman interpreter and another friend of mine. We reached our destination without trouble. Getting out of the car, Einaudi asked:

'May we take pictures in your country?'

'Why, certainly,' I said. 'Everything except military and strategic installations.'

A minute later a crowd had gathered about poor Einaudi, a crowd that was anything but silent. He was accused of taking a picture of an old lady who was selling ants (for rheumatism, perhaps?). There were some who went further, maintaining that the pictures were taken for espionage purposes. Anyhow, all four of us—the chief culprit and we three Soviet citizens—found ourselves in the local militia office. It was by no means the most exemplary militia office. We were held there forty minutes or so—they made some phone calls, asked questions, demanded the film, and only after we had done some vigorous persuading ('Son of a President! Director of a great publishing house!') and more phone calls had been made did they let us go, and even apologize. It should be pointed out that all during these forty minutes—spent in the company of some drunks from the market who were sleeping in the corner—our director of a great publishing house bore himself with great dignity and even sought to console me, repeating in Russian:

'These things happen. These things happen.'

Later on, in Moscow, they say he gave a very amusing account of the incident, adding that in Italy an affair of this kind would have lasted at least a couple of hours. In general he retained a very cheerful frame of mind; the

Half-way to the Moon

only thing he felt sorry about was that we never did manage to buy any 'works of folk art'—the marketwomen flatly refused to sell them. One of them told me frankly:

'If I'd known who it was for I'd have made something artistic. But this . . .'

Leaving San Gimignano, bidding farewell to its towers, which I doubt that I shall ever see again, I could not help thinking of my native Kiev. When you approach it today via the railroad bridge and admire its silhouette, you cannot but be gladdened by the radiance of the restored Lavra's cupolas and by the construction scaffolding on the Vydubetsky Monastery. The Cathedral of St Sophia, too, looks rejuvenated— the meticulous restorers have done a great deal of work on it. But if you stand with your back facing the cathedral you see on the opposite side of the square some nondescript fences and roofs. The golden-domed Monastery of St Michael once towered there. Now it is gone. In 1937 it was torn down. Torn down so that an office building could be put up in its place. The offices never got built, but the monastery from the eleventh century is gone. There are only fences and roofs.

I would not recall this deplorable incident of twenty-five years ago were it not that today some of those upon whom the fate of a particular architectural monument depends still believe that any church or icon is firstly 'opium for the people' and only secondly a work of art. About a year or a year and a half ago a rather influential Kiev newspaper carried an article suggesting that in this and that spot such-and-such eleventh- and twelfth-century churches and synagogues should be torn down. They spoiled the view, you see. A convincing argument, isn't it? . . .

What is most interesting in Italy are the disputes, the discussions, which Italians are especially fond of and at which they are undoubtedly masters.

I have encountered three types of discussions: (a) with illwishers who are bent on asking tricky questions, or em-

224

barrassing you; (b) with people who are not of our camp but who seek a common language, and (c) with friends, in the main communists. These last are, in a way, hardest to argue with.

On the last day of our stay in Rome, the poet Voznesensky and I had occasion to speak at an evening arranged by the Italy-USSR Society. Many people came, the hall was a small one, smoke-filled and hot. It was difficult to make a speech, especially towards the end of a hard day filled with all sorts of activities. After the report and our speeches, the questions began. It was at this point that it suddenly began to be fun. Most likely because those who took the most active part were a correspondent for the magazine *Tempo* and an American student who had once worked as a guide in our country at the American Exhibition in Moscow. Both of them had the same aim: to embarrass us. The next day, when we were already on the plane, we read with some pleasure an account of the evening in the official *Messaggero*: 'The Soviet writers amazed everyone with the artistry, humour and felicity of their answers, which were like rapier thrusts.' I still can't figure out why a paper by no means sympathetic to us decided to flatter us—it took no special artistry to answer questions of this sort: 'Is it true that after a certain speech by Khrushchev, Evtushenko was expelled from the Young Communist League?' Or: 'Why is not a single foreign book allowed into the Soviet Union?' It may be, though, that by artistry was meant the quickness of our replies and not their profundity. Humour is the best weapon against hostile people. Voznesensky and I tried not to forget this.

The most complicated of all, perhaps, was the 'round table' meeting at the Palazzo Marignoli. This was a meeting between Italian and Soviet writers, and it became chiefly a discussion of the problem of the 'commitment' of modern writers. In our language, the word 'commitment' sounds somewhat different and cruder than the French '*engagé*', but the meaning is clear: Has a particular writer joined a particular camp, what idea does his work embody, what course is he following and exactly what form does he use? The discussion aroused enormous interest; the hall was jammed—even the aisles were full, and people were not sitting but standing in the back rows, some even standing on the seats . . .

In my opinion, the most interesting speech of all was Pasolini's. He was more specific than the others and, I would say, more cutting . . .

Pasolini is a small, black-haired, black-eyed man with the simple, serious face of a worker or peasant; in the recent past (he is now thirty-five) he was a professional soccer player, but he is now a noted writer. He stood up and began to speak in a quiet voice. He expressed his dissatisfaction with Soviet literature. In his opinion, it is excessively naïve and sentimental (the Italians, who are by nature a sentimental people, never allow sentimentality in any form to enter art). He referred to Aksyonov's novel *Starry Ticket*, Evtushenko's poems and the film *The Ballad of a Soldier*.

'People working in Soviet culture,' he said, 'are striving hard in a period of crisis—and we anxiously and sympathetically watch their efforts—to overcome the inherited inertia of the Stalinist period by skipping what we call the decadent period. They are right to do this. But when they skip the experience of decadence, they find that, in some sense, what preceded it was romanticism understood as innocence and purity. This romantic, saccharine, humorous and, when it is at its best, classically naïve and pure air cannot satisfy us fully now. The Soviet situation, which has also affected our situation because of the close links between us, requires something quite different. The Stalinist period was a real tragedy for all of us. But then, Russian technical progress and the wave of amazing optimism that has arisen, pose problems that are just as serious for all mankind. The rocket to the moon, in addition to being a source of great pride for the Soviet Union, has also made us look anew at the world's sufferings, ignorance and poverty and I would say it makes us examine them from all sides. This is certainly not a simple situation. We expect Soviet writers to produce truly tragic works; works that are bitter and even cruel if necessary, in which all of this would be expressed.'

I have included this lengthy quote from Pasolini's speech because it broke up the academic atmosphere of the discussion and gave rise to the disputes. We did not agree that our literature is naïve and that it avoids the tragic (in this connexion we cited Fadeyev's *The Rout,* Kazakevich's *The Star, The Silent Don*). In his reply Pasolini tried to make things clear by referring to the Latin that had played a bad trick on him: It seems he had intended the word 'naïve' in the philologist's sense—'ingenuo', or 'natural'—and not at all in the sense of 'innocent' and 'childish', and that when he had called Chukhrai's art naïve he had meant to pay Chukhrai a compliment.

There was also some confusion about the Italian word 'tragico'; it is used in the sense of both 'tragic' and 'pertaining to tragedy', which are by no means equivalent concepts.

What does Pasolini want from our literature? Tragedy as a genre?

At first glance one might think that this is indeed the case: Pasolini's talent is merciless, and the philosophy of his works is the philosophy of inconsolability. But it turns out that this is not what he was asking of us (although, of course, he does ask it too). In his second speech he spoke about this directly, recalling the second trick his Latin had played on him.

'When I spoke of "tragedy" or "tragic", I did not have in mind tragedy as a literary genre. The greatest tragedies are those that make us laugh. I was speaking about a kind of tragedy that would not to the slightest extent deceive our thirst to know everything about the historical and political tragedy of recent years that Soviet writers experienced so profoundly.'

Tvardovsky answered this wish or demand of Pasolini's by saying that he always experiences 'a sense of awkwardness and fear when people engaged in a discussion attempt to solve problems that are difficult to solve even in the most friendly type of intimate conversation, or even alone at one's desk when one's mind is harnessed in the process of creativity'.

This is true; there are still things that one must think about alone before starting to write about them.

I very much regret, dear Pasolini, that that evening—or rather, night—when, after we had seen your film, you took us to supper in a small restaurant, you and I did not talk about what was most important to you and to me. It is possible that there were too many people there for a serious conversation, or perhaps we were simply tired and did not want to argue. But I know that this conversation—not an easy one—will take place; it cannot fail to take place. Before it does, I only want you and your friends (I hope they are our friends too) to know this: We understand very, very well everything that you consider tragic. But to talk about this, much less to write about it, is not all that easy. After all, we are not talking about the tragedy of 1, 2, 3, 10, 100 or even 1,000 people—we are talking about the tragedy of an entire people. And if our literature has not yet really taken up the complex, bitter and contradictory aspects of what we now call the period of the cult of the individual, this is only a matter of time. Soviet literature, for all its drive towards those things that are life-affirming (or perhaps even because of this), cannot ignore the tragic events of our life. It cannot because, as Tvardovsky said at the conclusion of his speech, 'In art and literature, as in love, one can lie only for a while; sooner or later comes the time to tell the truth.' Dear Pasolini, I would like very much for you to understand this before our next meeting and after it, if it takes place, so that you do not say, as you did at 'the round table', 'You can talk to the Russians, but you can't argue with them.' Incidentally, perhaps it was because of this idea of yours that we sat at night in the restaurant after seeing *Accatone* and spoke of anything at all but the main thing.

Italian communists, or at least those I have met (in Italy and in the Soviet Union), are not dogmatists and are certainly not revisionists. For them the decisions of the 20th and 22nd Party Congresses are just as important as they are for us.

For instance, they say:

'The decisions of these two Congresses are absolutely correct. The cult of the individual had to be unmasked, and you did this with the courage that is inherent in you. But we, too, must be understood. We are living under other conditions. We are in the capitalist world, and it has its own laws. You, or, in any event, your generation, know these laws only from books, but we encounter them at every step and every minute. The ordinary Italian is constantly under the influence of two mutually opposed ideologies. And so the Italian—the worker, employee, peasant—must choose. In order to choose he must know which is better. He reads the newspapers. He can buy any one he wishes: The *Osservatore Romano* from the Vatican costs the same as *Unita*. One says one thing, the other says something else. In one of them he reads that everything in the Soviet Union is bad and in the other he reads that everything there is good. At any rate, for a certain period of time that was what we wrote—that everything was good. Then it turned out that not everything, by no means everything, was good. We wrote that Stalin was great, wise and infallible. And they believed us; many people believed us. Now we no longer write about his infallibility but have a good deal to say about his sins, and people ask us, "What were you thinking about before?" You see, millions of people look to you. For them you are the first country in the world in which the working class has come to power. Therefore they want to know everything about you, the whole truth. They want to know the good things, the bad things and the problems. It is at this point that you do not always understand us. We are all delighted by the victories of Gagarin and Titov, but the average Italian, especially one who has been to the Soviet Union (and there are more and more of these all the time), unfailingly asks: "Why is it that these people who have sent a satellite around the moon still can't get rid of queues?"—and there are dozens of other questions. They are not idle questions, they are important ones. And we are obliged to answer them. But you bear first responsibility for answering. And you are often slow with your answer, or go off on side tracks. Meanwhile the enemy is making an answer—correct or incorrect— and the people often heed it. You don't take account of this.'

This is what many communists say. And then they start asking questions themselves. Why, why, why? One hundred thousand whys that sometimes made my head spin.

I must say frankly that it was very difficult for me to find answers to some of the 'why's'.

Somehow I got into a conversation with a young film director who came to the Moscow Festival in 1961. As we were talking about the film *The Island*, which won the first prize, he mentioned the names of two Japanese directors—Mitsogushi and Kurosawa—about whom I knew nothing. He was a little surprised, but when he then learned that I had never seen a single film by Bergman or Michelangelo Antonioni, he could not believe his ears.

'You haven't seen Antonioni's pictures?'

'No.'

'But why?'

I shrugged. 'We just haven't bought any of them.'

'You didn't buy any Antonionis? But he is now the most noted director. They are arguing about him all over the world. Not seeing his pictures is the same as not having seen, oh, say Fellini's *La Dolce Vita*.'

'But I haven't seen *La Dolce Vita*.'

He threw up his hands.

'You haven't?'

'No.'

'Well, you simply don't like movies, you're not interested in them. I can't believe that your people didn't buy *La Dolce Vita*. After all, it's a very serious, intelligent, terrible and also revealing film. I don't believe it.'

Another Italian asked me my opinion about Charlie Chaplin's latest films, *Limelight* and *A King in New York*. Once again I was obliged to say that I had not seen them and that they were not showing here.

'But why? Chaplin is one of the greatest artists of our times. Every picture he makes is an event.'

I didn't know what to say. I don't understand myself why Chaplin is not shown here. It is difficult to believe the story that his pictures are too expensive.

I was put in a rather difficult position on a third occasion, when I was asked why we don't publish certain writers. (At this point I recall how awkward a group of Soviet writers, including Panova, Granin and myself, felt six years ago when Alberto Moravia, who was visiting Leningrad, asked us some-

thing about Kafka. We looked at each other in silence; there
was nothing we could say in answer: At that time we had
never even heard of him.)

'I can understand,' said the person I was talking to—also
a communist, incidentally—'I can understand that you have
your own views about the tasks of literature and your own
publishing plans. I am quite willing to recognize that some
writers are closer to you and others more distant, while some
are completely alien. If it suddenly came into your heads to
publish Nabokov's *Lolita*, which is now a bestseller in
America, this would be simply absurd. But why are you so
slow to do Faulkner? Why don't you print Kafka? Why are
you so diligent in avoiding Albert Camus? In the final analysis, you are not obliged to print these authors in hundreds
of thousands of copies. But each of them is important in his
way, even Sagan, whom many say is not serious. After all,
these writers are extremely typical of their time, epoch,
state of mind. One doesn't have to love them; one may criticize them, may finally repudiate them, but one must know
them.'

Was this person right? I think he was.

We now publish a great many translations of foreign literature from almost all languages of the world, and in large
editions at that. But in spite of this, major events in foreign
literary life pass us by, or at best reach us only after a long
delay.

By the way, things are much better with translations of
Soviet literature in Italy than they were three or four
years ago and better than they are in other Western countries now. While for a time books by Soviet authors drew
attention only as something exotic or sensational, the situation has radically changed in recent years. The number of
writers who are translated is very broad and varied. Poets
are translated as well as prose writers. With my own eyes
I saw in the bookshops works by Tendryakov, Kaverin, Vs.
Ivanov, Ehrenburg, Kuznetsov, Aksyonov, Berggolts and Ait-
matov; plays by Arbuzov, Volodin, Khmelik; poetry by Evtushenko, Voznesensky, Zabolotsky, Okudzhava and Vinokurov.
And this list could easily be continued, for the largest
Italian publishing houses (Einaudi, Feltrinelli, Editori

Riuniti) follow our journals very attentively, and literally no more than two or three months after a work that interests them is published here they put it out there. Ah! if only our publishers were as efficient!

Now about movies. We buy a great many foreign films. We have seen first-class pictures by Rosselini, De Sica, De Santis, Visconti, Fellini, Truffaut, Otan-Lara, Bardem, Karel Zeman, Kavalerovic, but in addition to these there is a triumphant procession across our screens of all sorts of stuff that has nothing to do with art, such as *The Count of Monte Cristo* (in two parts, no less), *Oklahoma* and all sorts of other 'tuneful' bits. And this was money that might have been used to buy *Citizen Kane*, which the Americans consider to be the peak of their film art, or *Hiroshima Mon Amour,* by Alain Resnais, or *The Bridge on the River Kwai,* or Andrjez Wajda's *Ashes and Diamonds*—in a word, films that are milestones in the development of the world's film art . . .

Trattoria: At the risk of bringing thunder and lightning down upon me, I cannot resist singing your praises, sweet Italian *trattoria*, without which Italy is as unthinkable as it would be without oranges, monuments to Garibaldi and the triangular white ashtrays on your tables inscribed 'Cinzano' or 'Martini'. I am afraid that if for some reason all the *trattorias, osterias* and bars in Italy were to be closed, the Italians would mutiny. If such a terrible thing occurred, where would he, poor fellow, go to find out the latest news, drink a glass of wine, play dominoes, meet Carlo or Alberto, whom he absolutely must see about something, or pretty Lucia, or just sit in a corner and think about the things he cannot think about at home?

The *trattoria* is not a restaurant; it is a sort of club, a meeting place, a place where there is always a kind greeting for you, and where you are quickly served—excuse me, wrong word: When you go into a *trattoria*, you feel as though you had dropped in on your best friend, and that the greatest pleasure for him is to see to it that you are well taken care of. Ah, if only it was like that in the Abkhazia in Kiev! When you walk in, the smell of cooking, that bitter oily odour,

would be gone; they would not glare at you and say: 'Wait
a minute, don't drop dead. There's only one of me and there
are many of you.' The tablecloths would all be clean, the
waitresses would not fight among themselves over forks, there
would be no tasselled plush curtains and no ill-tempered
and haughty doorman. Ah, how fine it would be! What if
we proposed to Kiev's Abkhazia, as a sort of cultural exchange programme to provide better contacts, that it strike
up a friendship and a competition, with say, the Buca-Lapi
in Florence? Both of them are small and both are in cellars,
only the Buca-Lapi is a little older; it will be eighty this year.
A whole group of us went there once. You enter through
the kitchen, and things are always frying and crackling there,
but there are no fumes or smoke. You go into a room with
an arched ceiling; the walls are covered from top to bottom
with posters from travel and shipping companies—nothing
else, just posters. There are Italian, French, German, Spanish,
American, Argentine and Mexican posters, but there are no
Russian ones. 'Perhaps you will send us some when you get
home? We would put them up here over this table where
you are sitting now.' Instead of posters, our poets wrote out
some amusing lines on postcards, and our host immediately
put them on the wall. 'Now we have something to remember the Russians by too.' In exchange, each of us was given an
ashtray as a souvenir of the pleasant moments spent in this
convivial and inviting little cellar. Oh, I am afraid that
nothing would ever come of this friendship and competition,
and that when the director of the Abkhazia has seen these
notes I will never be allowed in there again.

Once I said jokingly to Sergio:

'Tell me, when communism has triumphed throughout
the world, what will you do with the *trattorias*? Will you
nationalize them or collectivize them?'

'Well, no,' he said. 'We will not be in a hurry to do that.'

I dare say this little 'ode to the *trattoria*' will arouse a
completely opposite reaction from some people. 'So we don't
have enough *trattorias* for him,' they will say. 'How terrible.
But Italy is not only noted for them, and not only for its
museums. It is a country of a fighting working class, a
country of mass strikes and unceasing unemployment and

hard times for the peasants. Why hasn't he said anything about this?'

These objections that I anticipate remind me of something said to me by a not very intelligent journalist with whom I was travelling in America. On the third or fourth day he began to complain:

'When are they going to show us the hovels? There's nothing to write about; everything's so slick, clean and comfortable.'

Somehow I don't want very much to be like him. We saw the hovels and the horrible sunless Chicago streets and the trains roaring by overhead, and we saw the classic unemployed on the Bowery in New York and some things worse. We were not in the south, but we saw on television the Negro schoolchildren going to school under the protection of the police so that they would not be torn apart by the brutalized crowd. We saw all this, and it all exists. But if you go to a foreign country seeking only this, why go? Somehow I am always ashamed when people take pleasure in the misfortunes of others. When I see hovels I am sorry for the people who live in them, and I take no delight in the fact that these dreadful houses and barracks still exist, even though they exist in the capitalist world that is alien to me. The journalist I have mentioned once said to me:

'I'll be damned—did you see that there are Negroes staying in our hotel? There were even a couple of them in the restaurant today?'

It seemed to me that he was actually offended that these two Negroes were not kept out of the restaurant; that would have made a fine little piece for the paper! In the south they do indeed keep the Negroes out, but this gives me no pleasure at all.

Well, enough—America will be along later; now let us go back to Italy and its life and to a subject they talk about as much in the *trattorias* as they do about soccer games and the latest trial of the Sicilian monks.

The struggle of the working class, strikes: It is true I never saw the people go out into the streets (I saw only a sparsely attended pro-fascist demonstration—about three dozen young people in cars and on motor-cycles carrying banners and slogans like *Fanfani plus Nenni equals Togliatti*), but about a year and a half ago in Moscow Alicata, one of the leaders of the Italian Communist Party, told me about what happend in Genoa in 1960. Pro-fascist elements attempted to organize something like a congress in this large port city. The people wouldn't allow it, and they came out into the streets, mostly young people. There were clashes and shooting, and the police intervened. There were not many details about this in our papers, but Italy talked of nothing else. The curious thing is that young people of the 'stilyaga' or 'beatnik' type—somewhat like Pasolini's heroes—took an especially active part in the fights with the neo-fascists. Alicata said: 'Those boys fought magnificently. But they still support us only when the class struggle is sharpest. This is a complex question, a very complex one. It is not all that simple to win them completely over to our side. They keep to themselves. They don't want to be guided, but they hate fascism and they are ready to fight it to the death. We communists must give serious thought to how to utilize this seething energy, how to guide it into the proper channels.'

Unfortunately, we managed to visit only one factory during all the time we were in Italy—a textile mill in Prato, near Florence . . .

On the very day we visited the Prato mill, negotiations were under way in Rome between representatives of the Italian General Confederation of Labour and the newly formed Government to halt the strike at the Michelin plant in Turin, one of Italy's largest tyre enterprises. The plant had been on strike since January. The management was trying to establish a lockout, but nothing, not even strike-breakers, did any good. Towards the end of the second month management gave in. The workers, who had not received a single lira for the two months, had won. It would be no exaggeration to say that the entire city helped them. A solidarity committee was organized. Money was collected at the stadiums, in the markets and simply in the streets. Even the city's largest theatre gave the proceeds from several shows to the strikers' fund.

All this tells us a great deal. These incidents are not exceptions: Strikes by factory, office, railroad and postal workers and, in the south, farm labourers are common occurrences. As a rule it is not management that wins. Italy is a country of highly active political struggle, a country where one cannot fail to take the working class and the Communist Party (which now has almost two million members) into account.

Italy is now going through a period of economic upsurge. This phenomenon is not characteristic of Italy alone. The Federal Republic of Germany and Japan—that is, the countries that suffered defeat in the past war—are also going through a boom period. The standard of living in Italy has increased noticeably. In the past five years the workers' wages have risen considerably, the number of unemployed has dropped, housing construction has been developed on a large scale and more and more Italian products are entering the world market. What is bringing this about?

There are many reasons. The following are the chief ones. In the first place, almost all the country's production equipment has been renewed as a result of the war. The process of replacing old equipment with new, a quite complex one in peacetime, has not come about from the good life, so to speak, since most of the country's plants and factories were destroyed. Italian production technology is now on a very high level. In the second place, the defeated countries were deprived of their colonies, and therefore they no longer bear the burden of colonial wars. And finally, the third factor, the military budget is relatively low: They do not have to spend money on missiles, since these are obligingly offered by America through NATO.

All of this has led to an economic situation that is known in the West as 'the economic miracle'. It should also be added that in this stage capitalism is obliged to seek new forms in the relations between capitalist and worker ('neo-capitalism', 'people's capitalism', 'social partnership', 'Olivetti paternalism'), but this requires special research that has no place in these sketches, which make no pretence to a scholarly approach.

How will things go from here? I will not attempt to answer that question either. I think that if we are speaking of Italy, a great deal depends not on what happens inside the country but on what happens outside it. The world is in a fever. And the kind of life that the Turin worker, the Roman schoolchild and the farm labourer in Luciana will have depends on what happens in the streets of Algiers, at the Brandenburg Gate, on Cape Canaveral and in the New York Stock Exchange.

And now I would like to tell about a young Italian from the town of Carpi, near Modena, whom I met in Moscow in the autumn of 1961. These were the circumstances.

In Carpi there is a factory that makes silk shirts that are famous all over Italy. Benito Gualdi, the director of this factory, is an expansive and wealthy man, and I would even call him democratic by nature. As in all Italian cities, there are petrol stations in Carpi as well as factories. One of these is tended by a young and very lively lad named Danilo Cremasci. The Italians are a communicative people, and, as I have already said, they love to argue about this and that in their *trattorias*. And so there was an argument in one of these *trattorias* between Benito and Danilo. What started it was that Gualdi had been to the Soviet Union not long before as a tourist. He did not care for our country, and instead of the two weeks he had planned to stay he remained only four days and then went off to Spain and Portugal. What was it that Benito Gualdi did not like in the Soviet Union? Many things, and some of them quite important. In the first place, none of the clocks worked in the Ostankino Hotel, where he was staying. In the second place, there were few taxis and in general no other cars in Moscow. In the third place, the cashiers in the stores used abacusi rather than cash registers. In the fourth place, Moscow housewives locked up their pots and pans in the communal kitchens; and so on in the same vein.

Gualdi delightedly recounted all this in the *trattoria*, and his audience listened open-mouthed. Danilo was indignant:

'That's all lies!'

'No, it's not lies!'

'I say it's lies!'

'And I say it's not!'

'How can you prove it?'

'What do you mean, how? I was there.'

'But I haven't been there. How can I check on you?'

'Check on me?'

'Yes. Maybe you're making it all up.'

'I'm making it up? OK! You want to check for yourself?'

'What do you mean by that?'

'Just this. You go to the Soviet Union; I'll pay your expenses.'

'You won't, either.'

'I will!'

'The whole trip?'

'The whole trip, hotels, everything!'

'What the deuce, then I'll go.'

And Danilo went.

Sounds like it's made up, doesn't it? But he did make the trip. I saw him myself. I don't remember how much or what was at stake, but Danilo was to confirm or refute what Gualdi had seen, and when he came back he was to tell about everything honestly. Surrounded by reporters and friends, Danilo Cremasci, petrol station attendant from the town of Carpi, got into a Rome-Moscow sleeper and set off for parts unknown.

He spent ten days in Moscow, days filled to bursting with all sorts of 'events'. Theatres, museums, clubs, meetings, and more correspondents. He was a young and energetic lad on his first visit to Moscow, and he ran about from morning to night like a squirrel in a cage. All the time he went on jotting, jotting, jotting. He amassed a whole stack of notebooks. He went to the Ostankino to check on the clocks (it would seem that they were not working), counted the taxis in the streets, studied Moscow cashiers—in a word, he was up to his neck in activity. And he was pleased with everything. 'When I get home, I'll have something to tell them,' he laughed . . .

I don't know how this story ended. I think that the silence of the *bourgeois* newspapers speaks for Danilo's victory over Gualdi. I had no chance to see Danilo when I was in Italy—

I did not get to either Modena or Capri—and Danilo probably did not know of our visit . . .

An amusing story, isn't it? And so thoroughly Italian.

Incidentally—and this is just in passing—Danilo, Corrado, a friend of mine and I made a trip to the Troitsko-Sergi-yevsky Monastery in Zagorsk on one of those autumn days. It seemed to us that this might interest them. After all, it is interesting to see what the religious situation is here, es-pecially for people from a country where the Church is so powerful. And then, of course, the architecture in Zagorsk is remarkable.

We made the trip, and it turned out that my friend and I were much more shaken by what we saw than were our Italian friends. Clearly, their homeland had already accus-tomed them to all sorts of religious fanaticism and zeal, and there was nothing here to surprise them. My friend and I simply could not believe our eyes.

It seems—who would have imagined it?—that sixty-odd miles from Moscow there still exists the most authentic example of the backward, hoary, dreadful Russia before Peter the Great. Old women without number are to be seen there, all dressed in black, and they are fleshless, nasty and malevolent. They wander about the courtyard, stand around muttering in the churches, line up in a great winding queue to kiss the remains of St Sergius Radonezhsky.

Under a crossfire of incinerating glances we elbowed our way into the church. Inside it was crowded in the gloom under the low, arched ceilings. Candles sputtered. The stern visages of saints gazed at us from the walls. At the shrine, holding the relics was a sleek priest. The line moved slowly and silently. There were men in the line, too, some of them young. All crossed themselves and bent down to kiss the remains. They looked at us with hatred and suspicion and called us 'pagans' and 'apostates'.

We went out into the yard. Crows circled in the trans-parent autumn sky around the wonderfully beautiful cup-olas, while down below, under the white walls of the cath-edral, a crowd of hysterical women clustered around a young emaciated 'fool of God' with rolling eyes. For some reason they were pouring water on his head, and the wet, miserable creature was smoothing the hair of a young woman who was clinging to him—he never took his eyes off her, and he was saying something, prophesying:

'There will be no war, no, no war, live in peace, love one another, that's the main thing, love, and don't look to me, I won't answer you, won't answer you anyway, you've got a bad eye, be off, be off, be off. It's the end of the Church, it's in its last days, pray, pray to God, because black days are upon us, war is coming and there will be slaughter and life will come to an end on earth, only flowers will remain and leaves, and grass, and the sea and the sky, don't ask me, I'll keep silence anyway for a year or two, or three, beginning this Sunday.'

And the old women called:

'Me, me, me, my own one, tell me—'

But their 'own one' pressed the clinging girl to him and they began hurriedly and ecstatically to rub noses. It was frightening.

A woman was wandering about the yard, a young woman, skinny and black-garbed like the others. With her arms stretched behind her she also was saying something, something about the end of the Church, about some deception and about a lack of faith in something.

We found ourselves at the centre of Orthodoxy, and it did not present itself to us as merciful, full of love and God-fearing but as an evil and hateful thing. There was here a sort of dark and dangerous power that still exists right alongside us.

I will long remember that day, the old women in black carrying their pouches, the shivering 'fool of God', the flourishing, handsome, sleek priests and the deacon's velvety voice. And the crows, the clouds of crows in the pure sky. And the ferocious glances.

I remembered that day six months later in Italy as I stood in the square before St Peter's Cathedral waiting for the appearance of the Pope. Every Sunday at exactly 12 o'clock he appears at a window of his residence and blesses the faithful. The enormous colonnaded square was jammed. When the hour struck and the tiny white figure of John XXIII appeared in a window from which a long red cloth had been hung, many people knelt. The Pope read a brief sermon, which was carried through the square by dozens of loudspeakers, raised his hands to the sky and disappeared. He left to the accompaniment of an automobile-horn salute.

Although a great many of the people around me were kneeling—there were many young monks and nuns among them with all shades of skin and habit—and praying to the Lord God, there was something 'modern' in all this. After the Pope had gone everyone, including the monks, began talking about their own secular affairs, and, dodging gaily among the cars, they set off in a noisy crowd down the broad and straight Via Conciliazione.

The power and influence of the Catholic Church are enormous, I know, and the forms in which religiosity appears in Italy are often monstrous (let us recall the church scenes in *Nights of Cabiria*, which, it is true, were considerably cut in the version we saw), but by comparison with what I saw in Zagorsk, the Sunday meeting with the Pope was to me simply a jolly spectacle or one of the offerings in an itinerary for tourists prepared by the Grandi-Viaggi Company.

Incidentally, the 'modern' aspect of the Catholic Church is to some degree its new weapon. The forms of influence on the faithful are changing. Even the Pope is no longer what he was. For example, they say (this is based on the Italian newspapers) that the eighty-year old John XXIII is very democratic and can sit down at the same table and even take a glass with his chauffeur. The Pope is a partisan of peaceful coexistence. After the launching of the Vostok 3 spaceship he held a special mass in Nikolayev's honour at his residence in Castel Gandolfo. Everything is in flux, everything is changing.

In America

I first made the acquaintance of the living America in my native Kiev just forty years ago, in 1922, which was not an easy or comfortable year. I was eleven, and I went barefoot (clogs and rope-soled shoes were then an unattainable luxury) to the fifth grade of Labour School No 43.

America—or, as we used to call it, the United States of North America—I knew chiefly through Mayne Reid and Cooper, through postage stamps (not very interesting— they were mostly pictures of Presidents) and also through ARA condensed milk, which was distributed to us children by Hoover's American relief organization (we also avidly collected the labels from the cans, with their pictures of Indians and bison). In addition, I would stop on my way to school to read, in a copy of *Proletarskaya Pravda* (printed on blue wrapping paper) that had been pasted to a wall, about the Greco-Turkish war and the Washington Conference. I had not yet seen any American films. This began about a year later, with *Master of the World, Queen of the Forests* and *Goddess of the Jungle*. Nor had I yet seen a single live American; at the ARA the milk and snow-white bread, soft as cotton wool, were handed out by Russians.

Then one fine day there came to Kiev, where he stayed with us (there were no hotels in the city, and my aunt worked in the library of the Academy of Sciences), no less a person than Mr Harry Miller Laidenburg, director of the New York Public Library, a spare man, no longer young, who carried in a bag over his shoulder a portable typewriter on which he typed out long daily letters home. When he came to the end of each line a little bell would ring, and at first I was constantly jumping up and running to open the door. When he arrived a bath was prepared for him. This was far from simple, since there was no firewood and not always water. We were very proud of this well-organized bath, and we hung out a clean towel, but our guest emerged after three minutes without having touched the water or the towel. Everyone was disappointed. After dinner he offered to help with the dishes, saying he always did that at home, but his offer was rejected. When he left we found fastened to his pillow with a safety pin either a dollar or a ten-rouble note, I forget which. We were all a bit offended, and at the same time touched. This is all I remember about Harry Miller Laidenburg, director of one of the world's largest libraries and the first American I ever met. I liked him.

The second American was working on the construction of the railroad station. I also worked there as an apprentice after attending trade school. His name was Borkgravink, but the workers called him Borshchgrivennik [borsch-penny] because he, like all the others, stood patiently in line in the workers' dining-room waiting for his plate of borsch. He was tall, thin, laconic and wore thick-soled shoes—which were objects of general envy—and as a consulting specialist on concrete he wrote extensive daily 'memos from Mr Borkgravink', which were hung in the office of the project director. I did not care very much for this American; he struck me as a bore.

After that I met no Americans, except for General Sherman—a medium tank in which I had a ride at the Front.

A good many years passed. Then in the autumn of 1960, or, to be more precise, on November 2, at 9.30 pm New York time, I stood for the first time on American soil, or more accurately concrete, at Idlewild International Airport . . .

I anticipate a thousand questions. Is it true that the Ku Klux Klan terrorizes everybody? Is it true that a crime is committed every six minutes in New York? Is it true that in the summer the temperature goes up to 110° in the shade? That every American has one-fourth of a car? That —no, I will not answer any questions like these. I will tell only about those things I saw with my own eyes, and I will use as few statistics as possible, even though—or perhaps precisely because—they love statistics so much in America.

I will begin with New York. No, I will begin with our group. We were not a delegation, we were tourists. There were twenty of us: teachers, journalists and engineers—what is known as the Soviet intelligentsia. Each of us had paid out a considerable sum, for which we were to spend fourteen days in trains and enormous buses in the north-eastern USA: New York, Washington, Chicago, Niagara, Detroit, Dearborn, Buffalo and then New York again. The leader of our group—let us call him for the sake of simplicity Ivan Ivanovich—was a wonderful man, but he had apparently been frightened since childhood. In addition, the American Express assigned to us as our guide a lively, poised man in a bow tie named Tadeusz Osipowicz, an *émigré* from Poland or the Baltic area; I will say at once of him that he was certainly in no sense a Mr Adams, of [Ilf's and Petrov's] *Little Golden America.*

It would be naïve, of course, to suppose that one can get even an approximate idea of America in two weeks. But it is possible to compare what one sees with what one has read. On this point everything depends on how the trip is organized.

I will say frankly that the Soviet tourist is not allowed to go everywhere. The south—New Orleans, Louisiana, Mississippi, the places where the Negro situation is many times more complicated than it is in the north—was not included in our itinerary. In New York, Brooklyn is strictly off limits. At Niagara Falls, where any taxi driver will offer to take you to the Canadian side for a dollar or so (there is an especially effective view of the falls from there), Tadeusz Osipowicz particularly warned us not even to contemplate doing this.

America is a special country. One Soviet woman writer who made a visit to America said: 'What struck me most of all about America was that there was nothing striking about it.' Somehow I don't believe that. In any event, a great many things struck me, although I was prepared for much that I saw, such as the skyscrapers, the vast numbers of cars, the lights of Broadway and the Sunday papers weighing a kilogram. But these very things: the gigantic buildings, the gigantic cities, the super-highways cutting across the country and travelled by thousands of cars, the twenty-storey department stores, the bacchanalia of constantly blazing advertising signs, the famous American service—in a word, all the abundance and wealth that overwhelms you immediately—make for difficulties, prevent one at first from getting to the deeper and more important things.

For in order somehow to get down to the essentials, in order to go a little deeper, if only relatively, one must not only visit the museums, go to the top of the Empire State Building or take pictures of Niagara Falls; one needs something else, something far more complex, and that is the ability to penetrate without prejudice, soberly and honestly, into everything you see. And this is by no means as easy as it seems.

On Both Sides of the Ocean

We are certainly not now on friendly terms with America, or rather with the United States. We, the two largest and most powerful nations in the world, are ideological and political enemies. Twenty years ago we were allies, but now we are enemies. This is a terrible word; one does not want to use it, and perhaps one even should not use it. Still, it is no use hiding one's head under one's wing. We do not trust each other, we are wary of each other and we accuse each other.

Under these conditions it is not easy to travel about the country, much less to write about it. And it is also difficult to communicate with people. Yet communication, be it with friends or foes, is the most important thing. It is only through communication that one can reach those depths, be they only relative, in which one is interested. And the most interesting things are life and what people live by. The Empire State and the Chrysler Buildings come afterwards.

The things our gentle Ivan Ivanovich feared most were deviations from schedules and arrangements. He was in a constant state of irrepressible tension and anxiety, was for ever counting us like chickens, and the worst thing that could happen to him was that someone would say: 'I don't want to go to the National Gallery, I want to go to the Guggenheim, or maybe just take a simple stroll along Broadway.' For some reason he dreaded this 'simple stroll' most of all.

On our first day in New York he set up the first production conference, the first 'briefing session', at the entrance to the United Nations Building after we had toured it. He asked Tadeusz Osipowicz to step aside for a moment and made a short speech about discipline, about the tasks and duties of a Soviet collective on foreign soil, about how so-and-so had been late for dinner on the very first day and had got separated from the collective so that he had to take a taxi, and about how this must not happen again or he would be required to take appropriate steps—true, he did not say what these might be. Like schoolchildren, we stood along the wall of the enormous building listening to him in silence, and then the accused began to justify themselves, voices gradually rose, an argument started, while Tadeusz Osipowicz stood apart and looked ironically at us. It was somewhat shameful.

245

Poor, poor Ivan Ivanovich. To some extent I understood him, and I was even a little sorry for him. After all, he had to keep track of all twenty of us; twenty people he didn't know and who had made one another's acquaintance only twenty-four hours previously, and we were not at home but in the City of the Yellow Devil (Gorky's term) with its gangsters, police and FBI. How could one fail to sympathize with him? Still and all, our kind Ivan Ivanovich forgot one thing: The local citizens were drawn to us Soviet people, they were anxious to talk to us, and we had no right to cut ourselves off and retreat within ourselves. They watched our every movement and listened to everything we said, and therefore we had to act completely natural, had to be ourselves. Excessive caution—let us call it that—does not bring people together, it drives them apart.

All the same, in spite of the strict schedules and arrangements, we managed to find out something about America. Not very much, but something.

And so (I have got off the track a little) let us begin with New York, even though so much has been written about it that I am afraid to begin. We spent all of five days there—a very short time. Strange as it may seem, one becomes used to this Babylon quite quickly. At first one is struck by the sckyscrapers, especially in Manhattan, but quite soon one feels that one has been looking at them, walking about among them and riding up to the 100th floor all one's life. The allegation that they are oppressive is nonsense (Hitler's Imperial Chancellery in Berlin oppressed me much more, in spite of its relatively modest dimensions), and many of them that have been built in recent years are very light (literally light!), airy and transparent. There is a great deal of glass in them, and they reflect each other in an amusing way. In the morning and evening, when they are illuminated by the horizontal rays of the sun, they are simply beautiful. Alongside them the skyscrapers of the beginning of the century seem somehow archaic. A Greek portico thirty storeys up merely makes one smile.

At the very top of the Empire State Building, the world's tallest building, there is an observation platform. For a certain sum, you are taken there in one of two high-speed elevators to look at the city through telescopes, drink coffee and buy souvenirs.

We went up too, of course. I must say that when you stand there above this city and look down at the scores of skyscrapers crowding the enormous expanse below you, at the tiny creatures and little cars crawling among them as though they were in canyons, at the East River, the Brooklyn Bridge and the Hudson, with its docks and ships—when you stand there like that, whipped by the wind, and look at that giant city or octopus city—whatever you choose to call it—you cannot but feel excitement. I had somewhat the same feeling once when I was on the peak of Elbrus. Beneath me stretched the Caucasus. Everything lay below me. Even Mount Kazbek was lower than I was. But while the beauty and magnitude of nature struck me there, the magnitude and beauty of man strikes one on the observation platform of the Empire State Building. After all, everything here was created by him, by his hands and his brain. One finds oneself asking the question: How many Empire State Buildings and Chrysler Buildings and bridges like the impetuous, light George Washington Bridge across the Hudson, how many useful things could be built with the money that is now spent on all sorts of Polaris and Honest John missiles and other jolly twentieth-century toys? (By the way, full-scale mock-ups of missiles stand in front of various military institutions in America, just as old cannons once did, and we even ran across one such missile in the concourse of Grand Central Station in New York. What is it doing there?)

Incidentally, America has splendid toys. I stood rooted for a long time before a 'railroad' window (this was in Brussels, not New York, but the toys were American). Three trains— a freight drawn by a Diesel, a passenger train drawn by a steam locomotive and a five-car express drawn by an electric locomotive—were circling around a complex network of rails. They disappeared into tunnels, raced across bridges, whistled, roared, stopped at stations or signals and never once collided. In the background was an airfield at which planes landed from time to time. But this was not all. When evening

came, lights appeared in houses and the locomotive headlights went on. I had to tear myself away from this spectacle. I had been dreaming about trains like these since I
was a child (like these? Trains like these were beyond even
my dreams), but I never had any. If I had the money now
I would certainly buy some. Not for myself, of course, but
for the eight-year-old son of a friend of mine; yet before I
gave him all this magnificence, I would lock myself in
my room with it so that no one would see what I was
doing.

Of course, the little soldiers are unbelievably intrig-
uing; they used to be called tin soldiers—I don't know what
they are made of now. They are of all types and sizes, nation-
alities and epochs. There are American Indians, Arabs, Napo-
leonic grenadiers, knights and Bersaglieri; the only ones I
didn't see were Red Army troops. Any young person could
be driven to insomnia by all sorts of costumes. For example,
the cowboy costume, which has a hat with a broad, curled
brim, fringed trousers, neckerchief and a pair of Colts in
luxurious holsters on a broad belt with metal ornaments.
To complete the picture one may buy a sheriff's star.

True, I saw some other toys made with no less skill. For
example, there is the Boeing bomber that flies and even
drops bombs, or the tank with a rocket launcher. On television they showed a tank moving towards the viewer. It
rolled up, levelled its cannon at you, and then: 'Buy the
best playthings for your children, the tanks of such-and-such
a firm!'

But back to Broadway. It consists mainly (along the stretch
between 34th and 52nd Streets) of theatres and cinemas.
Unfortunately, we did not get to the theatre (although the
Broadway theatre is the most interesting and characteristic
phenomenon of New York's theatrical life), but we did go
to the cinema on the very first day because we were lured by
posters showing the celebrated Elvis Presley—the idol of
American girls. This handsome, somewhat saccharine
twenty-year-old conquered America in a flash with his songs
of several years ago. If I am not mistaken, the world is in-
debted to him for rock 'n' roll. In a few weeks Presley became a millionaire, and his popularity reached such dimen-

sions that when he was called into the Army the US Defence
Department, according to the newspapers, received tens of
thousands of letters and telegrams from love-sick girls asking
that their idol not be taken away. But the Defence Department took him anyway, and he served his term. It was to
this event—Elvis in the Army—that the comedy we chanced
to see was devoted. The comedy was trivial but fairly amusing, and Presley danced no rock 'n' roll; he didn't even sing
very much, and the songs he did sing were pleasant. Most
of the time he sighed over the girl and she over him and they
kissed each other a few times, that's all. This diversion cost
us a dollar each, and also, I will tell you confidentially, it was
a subject of the lecture we had to listen to at that first 'briefing session' before the UN building.

We didn't go to the cinema any more, but we did get an
impression of them because there were twenty-one inch
television sets in our hotel rooms. The stations operate
twenty-two hours a day, and there are eleven channels. Did
we ever see fights! In bars, on the street, in trains, in luxurious hotels, at sea, underground, in the air, with tables
and chests turned over, rivers of blood and so many shots
that they were still ringing in my ears after I had been
home for two weeks. And how they fought! And the men,
how nimbly they flew across the length of the saloon, somer-
saulting, crashing through doors into the street and then,
wiping off their noses, back they would go into the fight and
escort their opponent out in the same style, but through the
window. Then the races and the chases! Not since I was a
child had I seen the like, only now the cars are longer,
lower and faster. We saw Rasputin, and Russian princes in
troikas, some sort of hypnotizer, sybaritic women laughingly
dealing with Tarzan-like men. The only trouble was that at
the most intense and decisive moment a pretty girl would
appear on the screen and for quite a long time would wash
her hair with some sort of special soap mixture, or else some
charming couple sitting on the banks of a beautiful lake
would reveal that they could not kiss each other until the
young man learned to take the right pill to kill mouth odour.
These and other scenes like them interrupt every film every
ten minutes. Every programme means advertising, and the

television companies live on the proceeds of this. Just imagine, it works. It even worked on us. All of us finally did buy
the magical 'Anacin' pills for headaches, although I, at least,
do not suffer from this complaint.

Yes, American television is a fearful thing. I had heard a
great deal about it, but only seeing it made me understand.
Indeed, just try not to hit your neighbour, try not to
knock him out with a well-aimed blow when from morning
to night your television set shows you how to do it. If you
don't do it to others, others will do it to you. There was a
great deal of talk about this at the writers' meeting in
Florence. There is even the new term 'semi-culture'—what
the English call 'mass media' and the Americans 'mass culture', which refers to a substantial part of Western films,
comic books, pulp fiction and illustrated magazines as means
for drawing people away from the practice of thinking, and
the first among these means, of course, is television, which
has pushed out books and conversation.

Incidentally, if we are to talk seriously about this, television is not the scourge of America alone. We don't have
the fights, the brawls or TV wrestling, that most monstrous
of sports—if this mutual torture can be called a sport at
all—but we do have something else: We drive our television
viewers into the depths of boredom with endless interviews
and amateur art shows that are as alike as two peas. Perhaps
this must be done so that the television studio can fulfil its
plan, but we don't have the energy to look at it any more.
For that matter, it is no easier to look at the viewers themselves. There is nothing more terrible than a family sitting
around the table in the evening with their eyes glued to the
television screen. Theatre, cinemas, books and guests are all
cast aside! They cannot tear their eyes away from the hyp-
notically flickering screen.

No, I recognize television only as a means of reporting. It
can show you Gagarin alighting from the airplane and striding along the red carpet, or Muscovites greeting Titov,
Nikolayev and Popovich, or it can take you to the Helsinki
Festival, convey to you what Jean-Paul Sartre has to say or,
in an extreme case, show you a film you have missed.

America's second scourge is the broad, dark stream of

police and detective literature. It is literally an overflowing sea. A good deal has been written about this already—about all those books with a pistol pointed at you from the cover—so it somehow pricks the conscience to say any more about it; but it cannot be ignored. I don't want to say anything derogatory about American book stores. There are a lot of them, and they contain a great many good, interesting and serious books. But good books are expensive, while all the detective rubbish costs pennies and practically throws itself at you, and the worst thing of all is that it is eagerly consumed, especially by young people. I am very sorry for the American boy. In general he is a good, simple and kindly sort, but I pitied him when I saw him sitting in the subway with a canvas bag on his knees and a publication in his hand that he had just bought for 25 cents at the news-stand and that he would throw away next day in one of the enormous trash baskets that stand on every street corner in New York. God, I pitied him. Of course, it is not obligatory to read Faulkner in the subway on the way to a training session or a game, but I fear that this boy does not read him at home either.

I want to run ahead a little to the close of our trip. We were travelling from Buffalo to New York . . .

The car door opened a little and the heads of two boys peeped in. They looked and looked, and then one of them said in broken Russian:

'You're Russian, right?'

'Right.'

'May we talk to you?'

'You may.'

'We'll be right back.'

Both boys vanished, but a minute later our car was full of young people. These were senior classmen, as we say in this country—children of about sixteen—who were making a trip to New York for a few days. They were being chaperoned by a teacher, not a young man, who I think was no less rattled than our Ivan Ivanovich by this unexpected meeting of two worlds.

The boys were lively, talkative and curious. Things went beyond the traditional exchange of badges, postcards and coins. It turned out that two or three of them were studying Russian, and one way or another we could converse.

I liked these youngsters. They behaved freely, naturally and gaily, and one sensed a certain culture in what they asked about, in what they said, and I understood that—perhaps not now, but in a few years—they would be reading Faulkner. The conversation jumped around; we talked about all sorts of things, about Moscow, New York, our jackets, about war, baseball, films (some of them had seen *Ballad of a Soldier* and had liked it very much), and about plans for the future. They talked about this last subject rather vaguely, or with a touch of humour: 'First I'll open a business, and then I'll take over from Kennedy.' Kennedy had been elected the week before. In general, Americans like and understand humour, but this 'first I'll open a business' made me prick up my ears, even though it was said in fun. Our conversation on this subject with the youngsters did not have any particular meaning, though, and we ended our meeting with renditions of 'Moscow Nights' and some song popular with American young people. In New York we parted, and in a jolly group brandishing their bags they disappeared into the crowd. It is of course difficult to say at this point which of them will take over from Kennedy, but it is unfortunately true that at least a quarter of them will try to 'open a business'.

The question of young people is an eternal one . . .

When we look at the young people of today, we sometimes like what we see and we sometimes shake our heads. I am not just saying that one meets lazy types and top students, beatniks and bookworms, careerists and gold seekers, boys in glasses and boys with bags under their eyes—this has always been true; I am talking about something more serious: about viewing of life and the search for one's place in life. There are some very serious children for whom study and work are everything. But there are also some among them who say: 'I love my job and I know it; the rest doesn't concern me.' For these work and study become blinders. There is also a more serious kind of split. There is the physicist, the good physicist, who is also interested in Heinrich Böll, goes to Richter concerts and the Mexican Exhibition, but God save him from politics. 'Oh, that. That's murky stuff,' he says. There is a still more complex and serious category of young people: those who are reliving, agonizingly, everything connected with the cult of the individual. These people say directly: 'We want to know the truth.' They have the hardest time of all.

But no matter what these kids are like (I am not talking of the 'scum' and the 'rot' that is to be found everywhere), their personal aspirations, the wish to become this or that, are as a rule not linked only with personal advantage or gain. There is also such a concept as duty to the people, to the country and to oneself. It seems to me that this is the chief thing that distinguishes our young people from Western *bourgeois* young people, and not the fact that ours go to Young Communist League metings while the Westerners dress in black sweaters and tight pants and dance rock 'n' roll and the twist.

I got into an argument about this in a comfortable little cottage not far from Washington. I had come there at the invitation of the Veterans' Friendship Society. We were invited by a tall, pleasant young fellow who spoke Russian rather well. He came into the restaurant in our hotel while we were at dinner, presented us with cards bearing the symbol of clasped hands, and told us that the members of this society would be glad to invite us to their homes in small groups of two or three. As in all such cases, Ivan Ivanovich lost his head, since these visits were not included in the schedule, but the young man said so sadly: 'Do museums and skyscrapers really interest you more than people?' that it was impossible to refuse him.

I don't remember exactly whose house it was. I was taken there in a car by a lady who drove in a thoroughly mannish fashion; as I understood it, she was the daughter of a Russian *émigré*. She said: 'Just call me Olga.' In the small and pleasant cottage there were about ten people, two of whom were Russian: Olga's husband, Lev Mikhailovich, a middle-aged and laconic journalist, and Volodya, a very lively lad of about twenty. Volodya and I got into a discussion that ended at 3 or 4 o'clock in the morning at our hotel room in Washington . . .

These arguments with people who are clearly not in sympathy with our system generally boil down to this: 'Why do you have one Party and not several? Why is abstractionism banned? Why don't they sell *The New York Times* on Moscow news-stands? Why do you jam the 'Voice of America? Where is your freedom?' And we answer: 'Why do you persecute the Communist Party? Why did you chase Charlie Chaplin out? Why do you maintain military bases all over the world? Why are you starving out Cuba? Why do you let your generals make inflammatory speeches? Is this what you call freedom?'

These exchanges don't do very much good; they only arouse mutual acrimony. It is much more important to learn something about the psychology of the person with whom you are arguing (if, of course, he is someone worth arguing with), to penetrate to the core of the question at hand (if, of course, it is a serious question), and, without boasting too much or trying to prove that, without exception, everything is better in your world than it is in your opponent's world, to demonstrate the rightness of your point of view.

It is difficult for me to judge how convincing I was that evening, but it seems to me that in the argument with Volodya about youth and its tendencies, I achieved a certain amount of success.

Not in the least do I idealize all our youngsters who go out to the construction projects—by no means all of them are guided by idealistic considerations; but a good many of them do go because they are doing the country some good. Is such a thing possible in America? I doubt it. The young American, even one who is searching and thinking, is concerned first of all about himself and about a career. For example, it is difficult to imagine one of our young men saying: 'I want this because it is advantageous to me'; this would simply be considered improper. Even if he thought this, he would not speak the words out loud; he would be ashamed to. On the other hand, the young American considers this completely normal. It is by no means his fault; it is required by the iron laws of the society in which he lives . . .

Volodya, of course, is not typical. There is too much Russian in him—too much of the desire to argue and to prove things. The American is nowhere near as interested in argument. In his pure state, the average—or rank-and-file, as they say nowadays—American (factory worker, office worker, student) is not very much given to cogitating and philosophizing. This is not primitivism, as some think, and not mental laziness; it is rather, I would say, a kind of infantilism (the American always even looks younger than his age), or, as one high-spirited Columbia University student said to me: 'We don't like it when they fill our heads with all sorts of rubbish.' Here, of course, it is necessary to decide what one is going to call rubbish, but, I repeat, the American—as opposed to the Italian, for example—does not like to argue. He prefers a friendly conversation over a glass of something strong, he likes jokes, jollity, fun. Generally he is by nature friendly, trusting, very simple and natural in his relationships, and if you are his guest he wants everything in his house to be simple and gay. He does not like tedium or anything official and formal.

I remember the black boredom that settled on our hospitable hosts and their guests in Buffalo when one of our tourist group (a university teacher) took out a notebook after the second glass of cognac and began a rather long recitation of figures on steel, iron, manganese and coal production in the Ukraine. And I remember, on the other hand, how delighted everyone was with another member of our group (a young Moscow newspaperman), who won everyone over with the first words he spoke to our host: 'I see you have the latest model Ford in your garage. May I go for a 100-mile-an-hour spin? He had his spin and delved into the engine with our host, got into a discussion with someone about recent baseball games, challenged someone else to a wrestling match. The Americans would not leave him alone, but our poor teacher sat in the corner with his figures in his pocket; everyone had forgotten him.

First of all, one should be oneself and not preach. Anyway, isn't being oneself the best sermon of all?

After all these thoughts about young people had been written down and when the whole manuscript was almost finished, I went to a Moscow showing of a film that forced me to return again to the subject of young people. This was Marlen Khutsiyev's film *Ilyich's Gate.*

I am not afraid of exaggerating when I say that this film is a great event in our art, a very great event . . .

A great deal has been written about young people and a great many films have been made about them, both in this country and abroad. But I have not read any book or seen any film that poses the question of the direction young people are taking as seriously and, I would say, with such personal interest and acuity.

Everyone has seen the excellent American film *Marty,* but not everyone has seen *Love at Twenty,* which consists of five separate episodes by five different directors, one French, one Italian, one German, one Japanese and one Polish . . .

The hero of the section directed by France's Truffaut falls in love in a very touching and pure way with a girl, and in the end nothing comes of it. All the complexity faced by the hero of the German episode is in that the girl he loves has borne him a son (he is a successful journalist, she is a telephone operator); in the Italian episode (directed by Rossellini) the young man is torn between two women, one rich, the other poor; in the Japanese episode the story ends with the murder of the heroine by the hero. Finally, moving on to the American film, we learn about the life of and follow the first timid love of that nice and charming American lad Marty . . .

All of them are merry some of the time and all have their moments of melancholy (except for the Japanese lad, who has constant control over himself—this film does not quite fit into the overall plan), and all of them are bored some of the time (in *Marty* and *Ilyich's Gate* alike: 'Where shall we go, kids, what shall we do?') but in only one of the films, Khutsiyev's, do the youngsters ask themselves: 'Well, and then what?'

The characters in *Ilyich's Gate* are bosom friends. They are happy when they are together. Their life is not too bad—it's not too good, either, but it's not too bad. They have jobs. One of them works in a factory, another in some sort of computing organization and the third does construction work. They meet in the evenings after work. They go out together and sometimes they drink. In general, they pal around. But complications arise in this life, which appears to have fallen into a pattern. Slavka has a wife and child, but he sometimes wants to 'hang around with the boys'. Apparently, his wife is clipping his young wings. Kolka has difficulties with the management; things have almost blown up in his face. Sergei suddenly falls in love with the daughter of an unlikeable and self-devouring highly placed comrade. Questions arise, as indeed they must. What is to happen next? What is the right thing to do? How can one avoid mistakes? In general, how is one to live?

I am boundlessly grateful to Khutsiyev and Shpalikov for not dragging in the old worker with the greying moustache who understands all and has a precise and clear answer for everything. If he had come along with his instructive phrases, it would have killed the picture. Khutsiyev and Shpalikov have taken another course, and a much more difficult one. Sergei asks the question: 'How shall I live?' of his father, who had died at the Front. This is one of the most powerful scenes in the picture. The father and son meet. What is this—dream, delirium, fantasy, hallucination? I don't know. But they do meet. The father is wearing his garrison cap and a poncho and carries his sub-machine-gun. The room is transformed suddenly into a dugout; soldiers are sleeping where they have fallen. There is a lamp made of a shell case on the table, and the father and son are drinking. The son says to the father:

'I wish I had been by your side in the attack when you were killed.'

'No,' answers the father. 'Why? You must live.'

And the son asks:

'But how?'

And the father asks a question in return:

'How old are you?'

'Twenty-three.'

'I am twenty-one.'

These words give you the shivers.

The father leaves without answering the question. His comrades are waiting for him. And they set off, the three soldiers, three comrades wearing their ponchos and their sub-machine-guns across their chests, marching through the morning in the Moscow of today. A car goes past, but they keep marching. They march like the three soldiers at the beginning of the picture—soldiers of the Revolution—marched along the streets of another Moscow, the Moscow of 1917. Their measured, pounding step gives way to another step—Red Square. The changing of the guard. The Mausoleum. The inscription: 'Lenin'.

There are many other lines, other turning points, other encounters, other complexities in the film, but all these lines, turning points, encounters and complexities come down to one thing: What happens next?

There is one answer: the same things that have been happening; the constant search for answers, the search for the correct path and the search for truth. As long as you are searching and asking the question of yourself, your friends, your father, in Red Square, you are alive. When there are no more questions there is no more you. A sated, successful existence with no disturbances and no questions is not life.

This has turned out to be something like a film review. Very cursory, but still a review. This wasn't my intention; I wanted to do something else. I wanted to find an answer to the question: 'What, in the final analysis, are our young people like? How do they differ from young people in the West?' Khutsiyev and Shpalikov have given the answer for me.

I have no doubt that there are youngsters like this in the West too; it couldn't be otherwise. They are to be found in Cuba, America, Italy, France—but this is the first time they have appeared in our art. I think that this certainly has some significance.

In the third day of our visit to America we set off at 9.30 in the morning from Pennsylvania Station for Washington in a train called *The Executive*.

The passengers dozed or leafed through magazines. At the end of the trip the whole car was as full of magazines as abandoned German headquarters used to be full of documents. I sat at the window and recalled my childhood.

I once had a friend called Yasya. He and I published a 'newspaper of the future'—it was dated 1979. It was called *Radio*. We brought out some ten or twelve issues. Unfortunately, the whole file is gone. The Germans burned it, along with the house we used to live in. More than thirty years have gone by since then, and fewer than twenty years remain until 1979, but when I recall those days now it is difficult not to smile. Reality has so far outstripped all our childish dreams and fantasies. We were ahead of reality in only one thing (and after all, there are still seventeen years to go before 1979), and that was in space flight. We had already been to Mars. But the sinful earth remained at the level of the 1920s. We had not even built any subways. We solved Kiev's transportation problem by increasing the number of street-car lines to 100, which seemed like enormous progress to us then. We also waged our wars in an old-fashioned manner. In 1979 we were fighting against the Anglo-Acans (the British and the Americans). I don't recall what we were fighting about, but I do remember that the battles, which were being fought in Alaska, exactly resembled the battles of Champagne and Verdun, all the more so because we cut our pictorial material out of the old Neva magazine and the French *L'Illustration*.

Then we grew tired of our newspaper, we were fed up with it, and in its place came a 'round-the-world' Moscow-Vladivostok-New York-Paris-Moscow railroad. A bridge had been built across the Bering Straits, and the trains were borne across the Atlantic, which had not yet been traversed by Lindbergh, on fast ocean-going ferries. On huge sheets of paper left over from the newspaper we drew up schedules for this railroad. We had express trains, high-speed trains, ultra-high-speed trains, mail trains and even combined freight- and passenger-trains. The schedules were drawn up according to all the rules. Stations wih restaurants were indicated by a crossed knife and fork and sleeping-cars by little beds. We never completed the project. We got through Siberia, Alaska and Canada and arrived at Chicago, but at this point summer came and vacations started, which meant the Dnieper, a boat and much more attractive things. Thirty years later, sitting in the upholstered seat of *The Executive*, I was reminded of this incomplete project. When we arrived in Chicago a few days later I bought a New York-Chicago timetable of the Baltimore and Ohio Railroad, put it in an envelope and sent it off to Moscow to the person who is no longer Yaska but Yakov Mikhailovich, geologist, historian and master of several languages, yet who, despite his years, has not lost his sense of humour. Perhaps he would suddenly be seized with a desire to complete that important and necessary work that was interrupted thirty years ago. Alas, for reasons that I do not know the envelope did not reach the addressee; humour is obviously not held in high esteem at border posts . . .

Washington is the most un-American of all American cities. It has almost no industry, the streets are broad and green and the buildings are low. It is a quiet, calm, early-retiring city of officials . . .

We strolled past the graceful fence around the White House, which was beautiful and calm in the shadows of ancient lindens and elms; on the next day, November 8, there was to be a decision about who would be the next occupant of that house, Nixon or Kennedy. Under the Constitution, the Washingtonian has no electoral rights, but he may listen to the radio and watch the television set. On that evening we too sat at the television set and listened to Kennedy and Nixon.

Two young and energetic millionaires. Which of them would be the victor? What would the victory of either bring the world?

For us Soviet people, this competition between two powerful capitalists had little meaning. Wasn't it all the same no matter which one won? One was supported by certain powerful trusts and monopolies and the other was supported by others. The struggle between the elephant and the donkey (the symbols of the two rival parties, the Democrats and the Republicans), a struggle that costs tens of millions, often seemed funny and naïve to us. But Americans have a different opinion. The people of left-wing persuasion whom we met definitely favoured the candidacy of Kennedy. He, they

On Both Sides of the Ocean

said, was younger (forty-two years old! There had never been a president so young), more progressive, had a good war record and in general, dear friends, it is rather difficult for you to figure out our democratic politics. Believe us, we know whom to vote for. On the evening of the 9th we sat before the television screen like all Americans and followed the counting of votes, and we, too, 'rooted' for Kennedy.

Two years have passed since that day. A great deal has changed in the world in that time. There is still that same tension between America and us. Queues of thousands wait in New York to get tickets to the Bolshoi Ballet, the Moiseyev ensemble gets ovations. Muscovites waited impatiently for the arrival of the New York City Ballet, it was impossible to get tickets to Van Cliburn concerts, *Moby Dick* with Rockwell Kent's illustrations was sold out in one day, but we still cannot come to agreement at UN sessions or at Geneva.

I remember a picture in an American magazine in the early days after the war: It showed Uncle Sam reaching across the ocean to shake the hand of a blond young fellow in a Russian shirt called Ivan. The caption was : 'Our friendship is the foundation of peace'. This is what they were writing in 1945. Should this not also be true in 1962?

In the Southern part of the Arlington National Cemetery six bronze American servicemen, standing on a pedestal of polished labradorite, are raising the Stars and Stripes on the peak of Mount Suribachi on the island of Iwo Jima. This incident occurred on February 23 1945, on a distant Pacific island, and now, cast in bronze, it symbolizes the glory of the American Marines. Three of the six men died on that same island. The fourth, Ira Hayes, an Indian, died in 1955 and is buried not far from the monument. The two others are still living and can come at any time to look at their own bronze images.

One may like or dislike this monument. It is very dynamic, and at the same time it is photographically realistic (they say that Weldon, the sculptor who made it, actually used photographs while he was working on it), but when you look at this monument you are led into thought.

261

The whole world knows of the contribution that America made to the struggle against fascism. The name of Franklin Roosevelt is respected in all corners of the globe. It is true that the United States did not know the horrors of occupation, destruction or barbaric bombardments, but American soldiers died at Pearl Harbor, in the Philippines, in the Persian Gulf, on the Solomon Islands, at Monte Cassino and in the Himalayas. Three hundred thousand young Americans will never come home again. Americans knew not only the triumph of victory but the bitterness of defeat at Pearl Harbour, in the tragedies of Corregidor and Bataan and in the alarming days at the beginning of 1942, when it seemed that the Japanese would soon be in Australia and at the shores of America itself. These days were much harder for us, and I have no intention of belittling our contributions in the war, but still we Russians will never forget the aid given us in those difficult days—the Sherman tanks, the Airacobras, the Studebakers, the canned pork, and the things we didn't see at the Front that went to our industry.

One recalls all this when one looks at the monument to the six American servicemen. After all, they fought as we did against fascism. They fought far away from their homeland knowing that all was peaceful at home. Three of them were killed. For what? Was it so that swastika armbands might appear on the sleeves of American youths, so that portraits of Hitler might hang in the headquarters of the American 'Birchite' Nazi organizations and so that the familiar '*Sieg heil!*' might ring out again? I know that these organizations do not have many members, and that the majority of Americans feel contempt and revulsion towards them, but they exist, and it is difficult not to think of this as one stands at the monument to people who fought against fascism, which had more hate for mankind than anything else on earth.

Two weeks in American Express buses.

'Ladies and gentlemen, ladies and gentlemen, do not hang back. We have two more museums, the aquarium and a visit to the Chicago Sun.'

On Both Sides of the Ocean

Museums, museums, museums. Let us see some people, for goodness' sake! Have a look at how they live, what they are doing and what they are thinking about.

The same Kiev newspaperman—I will call him K (the member of our tourist group who was worried because he did not have anything to write about, since they had not yet shown us the slums)—began to give lectures immediately upon returning home. There were posters all over town proclaiming 'America, 1960'. I went to one of these lectures. K dealt very thoroughly with slums, unemployment, poverty, the New York streets that no light ever reaches, hard labour conditions, the high cost of apartments, low wages and strikes. He was asked about the prices of goods. He replied that he had not looked into this. A whisper ran through the hall. A young man asked shyly what the alcoholism situation in America was, did they drink much there? K answered:

'A great deal. In Washington—no, excuse me, in Chicago —we saw one drunk who could hardly stand up.'

The audience burst into loud laughter. I was ashamed, although I understand that, thank God, one does not meet people like K at every step.

Another Soviet journalist, who had lived in New York for about four years, said to me:

'America is truly a land of contrasts. The contrasts are extremely striking. Poverty and riches, beauty and monstrous ugliness exist side by side. But when one speaks of contrasts one must still retain some sort of proportions of black and white. I ask you when you write about America that you retain a balance of fifty-fifty, as they say here. Do not write that American young people are interested only in rock 'n' roll and baseball. They are interested in these things, even carried away by them, but, believe me, they also read newspapers and books and magazines as well. They will also read your article. Take this into account so you won't have to blush later.'

Then there was another journalist, an American this time, but one who knows Russian quite well and who has visited this country a number of times. He asked me (this was two years earlier, in Italy) if I planned to write about America, and if I did would I please not end my article with lines about the hard-working, talented and brave people whom the author came to love in spite of everything even though he was only in the country a short time.

'I will start reading your piece from the end,' he said, 'and if I find those lines there I won't read it because it won't be objective.'

I promised him to end my essay with some other phrase, and I asked him in turn how he concluded his articles on the Soviet Union. He smiled and said:

'In various ways. But I once ended one in exactly that way, because I learned the phrase in your country. Therefore I am forewarning you.'

He wasn't a bad fellow, and as I found out later he kept to the fifty-fifty principle in the articles he published in a not very pro-Soviet magazine.

Personally, I don't intend to keep to any balance. What is more, I am going to do everything I can to avoid generalizations (I saw too little), and I will attempt to figure out what I saw and to figure out those thoughts and associations that came to me from various phenomena or from various meetings in America. I don't pretend to anything more.

During the two weeks I was in America I did not make friends with or get close to any Americans. It was quite different with the Italians in Italy. My 'Italian notebook' is full of addresses, but the 'American notebook' has only two or three telephone numbers. And this in spite of the American sociability and simplicity in relationships.

The following conversation, which I have especially left until just before the final curtain, took place in one of the uptown sections of New York, where there are no skyscrapers or advertising signs, in the area of Lexington Avenue and 125th Street, nor far from the Harlem River, in one of the little saloons there.

It was my last evening in America. I wanted to spend it by myself. I stepped out of the hotel, walked along Broadway, which by this time was beginning to be empty of life, went as far as Grand Central Station, descended into the subway, boarded a train and, having decided to ride ten stops, got out at 125th Street.

On Both Sides of the Ocean

It was 12 o'clock. There was no one on the street, which was rather dark. Something like the Moscow of Tverskaye-Yamskaya Street. Street lights few and far between, some fences. I walked with no particular destination in mind. At the corner of two narrow streets I discovered a saloon. It, too, was almost empty. At a table off in a corner two unshaven middle-aged men in blue overalls were drinking beer. Behind the bar, with long shelves of varicoloured bottles as her back-drop, was a very good-looking mulatto. On this side of the bar, leaning their elbows on it, were two fellows: one, somewhat the older of the two, in a short leather jacket, the other, the younger, a Negro in a very bright-coloured check-ered sport shirt. The three of them were talking quietly about something. There was some music playing, something jazzy, syncopated.

I walk up to the bar, put down a dollar and raise one finger. Continuing to talk, the good-looking Negro girl pours me out some whisky in a tall glass. I carry it to an empty table by the front window and go back for a glass of pale beer and a tiny ham sandwich.

I sit at the table sipping the beer and smoking a Belomor: I had no more money for cigarettes—had to leave some for the subway. No one takes any notice of me. The two middle-aged men in overalls pay their bill and leave. The other two go on talking. I look at the posters hung about—adver-tisements for White Horse whisky, Martinis, Coca-Cola. I am sitting alone, in uptown New York, in a saloon, drinking whisky. If Ivan Ivanovich knew . . .

The Negro said good-bye to the good-looking barmaid and left. The fellow in the jacket tarried, counting his change. Then he ordered another glass of beer and, looking around him, sat down at my table. The girl wiped the bar.

The man who had sat down—he was not young, had grey hair on his temples and deep creases about his mouth—drank his beer and smoked without saying a word. After finishing his cigarette and stubbing it out in the ashtray, he suddenly looked up at me. There was mild surprise in his eyes.

'Belomor?' he asked, his eyes pointing to the stub in the ashtray.

'Belomor,' I said.

Pulling out a pack, I gave the bottom a tap with my finger.

'Lieutenant Patrick Stanley,' said the fellow in the jacket. 'Flying Fortress. Gunner-radioman. Poltava airfield.'

Two more glasses made their appearance on the table.

Patrick Stanley—Flying Fortresses—Poltava airfield. So it turns out that you and I saw action together. You in the air and I on the ground. And now here we are sitting in uptown New York drinking beer. You have good beer; it's strong. And cold. Why are you laughing? You like vodka better? You're right. Where'd you learn to drink it? In our country, no doubt? In the hospital? No, in the hospital you learned to drink straight alcohol. The nurses brought it to you—admit it. I was in the hospital too, I know. You were in Poltava and I was in Baku. So that's the way it was—and seventeen whole years have now gone by. What kind of work are you doing now? You fix television sets? Well, that's a pretty good job. Pretty good or not, I don't have enough money. There's never enough money, though. Millionaires don't have enough either. And then there's my son. Seventeen, and he already wants a car. For two or three hundred dollars you can buy a used one, quite a decent one, but that's not for him: He's got to have a new one. Quit school, the fool; got a job in a store. Why go to school, he says, when you can make money without going to school. Funny, I myself received a letter from a friend in Australia—her son says just the same thing: Why go to school when you can be working. Yes, young people are a problem today. But then, fathers always criticize their children: This is not right and that's not right—we were better. Yet all in all we were probably just the same. Well, OK, let's have another round. No, let me pay, you're my guest after all. When I come to see you, you'll stand treat, but here I'm host. Yes, I'd love to go to Russia. I'll scrape together some cash and shove off with the wife to Poltava. Then again, no. Better without the wife. Because I may run into Klava—there was a nurse there named Klava—no, I'll go alone, without the wife. Is that the right thing to do? And on my way to Kiev I'll stop and visit you. What kind of work do you do there?

Architect? That's pretty nice. Probably have a decent income if you've been able to come here. Here and back by plane—I imagine that's a pretty penny. How about it, another round? Don't look at us that way, Betsy—this is the last one; we'll be leaving in a minute. Ah, it's too bad your plane leaves tomorrow; otherwise you could spend the evening with us, see how an American like me lives. But what do you think of America? Like it? No, let's have only the truth. Our papers, for instance, tell a lot of lies about you, but I don't believe them. What about yours? It's altogether a shame, damn it. Just who thought it up, this cold war? When there was a hot one we were friends; the cold one began and we're on the outs. Who wants this? You? But I know you to be good guys. And we're not so bad either. What did we fall out over? Berlin? What do I want with Berlin? I surely don't want to go to war over it. I don't want to go to war over anything. I've had my fill of fighting. And I don't want Jim to go to war. I'd rather see him buy his car after all, and take his girl riding in it. He's a great kid, honest. I am sorry, though, that you're leaving tomorrow. If you weren't, the three of us could go somewhere and have some fun, eh? Of course, we could take something from Betsy now and go up to my place; my wife's gone to her relatives in Baltimore. Well, OK, I know you have to leave tomorrow. I've got to be getting up early, too. Too bad you won't have a chance to meet Jim. You'd like him. He even knows a few Russian words—'sputnik', 'lunik', 'davai-davai', 'vodka'. He's a nice kid. No, doesn't drink yet. Well a drop when he's with his pals. My boy's an athlete, plays hockey, swims well. We're going, Betsy, we're going, don't be mad. You can lock up. Just remember today's date—first time you've had a Russian in your place. This doesn't happen every day.

The street was by now quite empty. We hated to part, so we walked to the next subway station; the trains here run all night.

Ah, Patrick, Patrick. Seventeen years ago you and I were seeing action together, you in the air and I on the ground, and now here we are marching along the echoing streets of late-at-night New York. And it feels good to be with one another, we hate to part. Yet our countries are for some reason not on friendly terms. Why not? You and Jim must pay us a visit; I'll show you a lot of interesting things. Won't spend too much time taking you around to museums, but I will introduce you to some good fellows. I'll tear you and Jim away from your tourist group and we'll drive over to see one of my friends. He and I were once in the same hospital together in Baku, and now he's an electric welder. You can't imagine how happy he'll be to meet you and Jim. And not because you're Americans, but because you're regular fellows. And he is, too. You'll be friends right off the bat. He'll do a bit of showing off (regular fellows or not, you're still Americans, and he'll want to put his best foot forward), he'll turn the knob of his television set, praise his wife and little girls, praise me, his friends and his job. Then these same friends will show up, there will be a rush to get to the delicatessen before it closes, there'll be a shower of questions, everyone will be clapping you and Jim on the back (and my friends, I want you to know, have strong arms); then Jim and some of the younger fellows, planting their elbows on the table and pressing each other's palms, will start a test of strength—'Come on boy, do your stuff!'—and everyone will be yelling and laughing, and afterwards there's certain to be singing and sometime after 3 o'clock in the morning we'll make a futile attempt to catch a cab and, walking somewhat unsteadily—a bit more so, I expect, than now—we'll start wandering around Kiev late at night, just as we are now around New York, only there'll be a few more of us, and someone's absolutely certain to come out with the song 'Do the Russians Want War?' and you and Jim will shout in response: 'The Americans don't want it either!' —and we'll have fun and enjoy ourselves and, just like now, will hate to part.

We reach the subway. We go down. The trains run infrequently at this hour. We both light cigarettes. Near a chewing gum dispenser someone is asleep on a bench, his legs tucked up. A Negro in blue overalls is sweeping the platform. It's already after 2 am. Poor Ivan Ivanovich.

The train arrives. 'Well, good-bye, Patrick. Say hello to your Jim for me.'

I step into the compartment. We get under way. The train enters a tunnel.

Patrick Stanley. Flying Fortresses. Gunner-radioman. How sorry I am that I did not manage to meet you, that this whole story of the trip late at night, the saloon, the beautiful Negro girl, the pack of Belomors is something I invented. There was no saloon, there was no Negro girl, there was no Patrick. There was only the wish that it had been so.

The stewardess, a pretty girl wearing a dark-blue service cap, walked quietly down the aisle.

'We are now over Paris. We'll be in Brussels in an hour.'

I looked through the porthole. It was beginning to get light. You could see nothing; clouds, unbroken clouds. It must be raining over Europe.

Moscow in two days. There'd be snow and light frost. And friends—standing there waving their caps: 'Welcome!' In a moment the embracing and kissing would begin. And then questions. Questions, questions, a hundred thousand of them. And they'd all have to be answered. Oh, it is hard.

Translated by Robert Potts and Leo Gruliow

Original Russian Sources

Andrei Voznesensky, *Parabolicheskaya ballada*, from the collection 'Scrivo come amo' ('Pishetsya kak lyubitsya'), Feltrinelli, Milan, 1962

Bella Akhmadulina, *Vulkany*, from the collection 'Struna', Moscow, 1962.

Evgeni Vinokurov, *Yest na vsekh vokzalakh kniga zhalob . . .* from the collection 'Lirika', Moscow, 1962

Andrei Voznesensky, *Pozhar v arkhitekturnom institute.* Translation based on variant texts: from the collection 'Treugolnaya grusha', Moscow, 1962; from the collection 'Scrivo come amo', ('Pishetsya kak lyubitsya'), Feltrinelli, Milan, 1962

Andrei Voznesensky, *Osen*, from the collection 'Parabola', Moscow, 1960.

Andrei Voznesensky, *Lobnaya ballada*, from the collection 'Treugolnaya grusha', Moscow, 1962

Andrei Voznesensky, *Tumannaya ulitsa*, from the collection 'Mozaika', Vladimir, 1960

Andrei Voznesensky, *Antimiry*, from the monthly *Znamya*, No 4, 1962

Alexander Solzhenitsyn, *Matryonin dvor*, from the monthly *Novy mir*, No 1, 1963

Yuri Kazakov, *Adam i Eva*, from the monthly *Moskva*, No 8, 1962

Vasili Aksyonov, *Na polputi k lune*, from the monthly *Novy mir*, No 7, 1962

Andrei Voznesensky, *Krony i korni*, from the collection 'Scrivo come amo' ('Pishetsya kak lyubitsya'), Feltrinelli, Milan, 1962

Andrei Voznesensky, *Vecher na stroike*, from the collection 'Mozaika', Vladimir, 1960

Original Russian Sources

Andrei Voznesensky, *Ty s tyotkoi zhivyosh* . . . from the collection 'Mozaika', Vladimir, 1960

Victor Sosnora, *Delfiny*, from the monthly *Oktyabr*, No 9, 1962

Boris Slutsky, *K diskussii ob Andree Rublyove*, from the monthly *Yunost*, No. 2, 1962

Bulat Okudzhava, *Bud zdorov, shkolyar*, from the collection 'Tarusskie stranitsy', Kaluga, 1961

Yuri Nagibin, *Pogonya*, from the monthly *Moskva*, No 9, 1962

Evgeni Evtushenko, *Tainy*, from the monthly *Novy mir*, No 7, 1962

Evgeni Evtushenko, *Stuk v dver*, from *Literaturnaya gazeta*, August 24 1961

Evgeni Evtushenko, *Ya shatayus v tolkuchke stolichnoi* . . . from the collection 'Vzmakh Ruki', Moscow, 1962

Evgeni Evtushenko, *Yumor*, from the collection 'Yabloko', Moscow, 1960

Evgeni Evtushenko, *Nasledniki Stalina*, from *Pravda*, October 21 1962

Victor Nekrasov, *Po obe storony okeana*, from the monthly *Novy mir*, Nos 11 and 12, 1962

Notes on Authors

ANDREI VOZNESENSKY (*see* Introduction), the best of the post-Stalinist generation of poets, was born in Moscow in 1933. He attended the Moscow Architectural Institute in 1957, and published his first poems in 1958.

BELLA AKHMADULINA, who is in her late twenties, is of Tartar and Italian origin. She was expelled from the Gorky Literary Institute and sent to Central Asia in 1957. It took five years for her one book of verse (*Struna*, Moscow, 1962) to be approved for publication. Her poetry readings have attracted enormous audiences. She is greatly admired by the new intelligentsia, both as a poet and as a romantic figure; she is the subject of some of the best love lyrics written by her former husband, Evtushenko.

EVGENI VINOKUROV (b. 1925) was a battery commander at the Front in the Second World War. He published his first book of verse (1951) during the Stalin era; it contains, as he says, 'not a word about Stalin'. Vinokurov, who is exclusively a lyric poet, is not engaged in public life; he is less concerned with verbal innovations than other young poets. His verse has a deceptive smoothness and naïveté.

ALEXANDER SOLZHENITSYN's first published work, *One Day in the Life of Ivan Denisovich*, was written in 1959 but allowed to appear in print only in November 1962, by permission of the Central Committee of the CPSU. Despite the extraordinary national and international impact of this novel about a Stalinist prison camp, Solzhenitsyn refuses to give interviews to journalists; he appears to want the sort of privacy, far from the big cities, sought by the hero of his semi-auto-biographical story, *Matryona's Home*. He lives in a village near Ryazan where he has been a teacher of mathematics and physics. He is now reported to be gravely ill. The bare facts of his life are as follows: he was born in 1918 in Rostov-on-Don of intellectual parents, graduated in mathematics at Rostov University, and served as an officer in the artillery during the Second World War. He served at the Front from 1942 until February 1945 when he was arrested in East Prussia on a political charge. He spent eight years in Soviet forced labour camps, was released in 1953, 'in the absence of a *corpus delicti*', but was rehabilitated and allowed to return from exile only in 1957.

His place in current Soviet literature is somewhat anom-alous. He was exempted from criticism for *One Day* and even singled out for praise by Ilichev and Khrushchev during the cultural offensive of 1962-3. This is very odd in view of the continuing campaign against writers who portray Soviet re-ality, both past and present, in extremely 'dark colours'. Nobody has portrayed life under Stalin in darker colours than Solzhenitsyn. One must assume that the exception made for Solzhenitsyn is due to the fact that the approval of the Party Presidium is sacrosanct even though it plainly contra-dicts the line as applied to other authors. If *One Day* is a 'good' work, however, then *Matryona's Home* is a 'bad' one. It has been much attacked for its pessimism and its 'historical inaccuracy'. For example, the playwright V. Koz-hevnikov, (*Literary Gazette*, March 2 1963) expressed 'great spiritual grief' after reading the story: '*Matryona's Home* was written by the author in a state in which he was not yet capable of understanding the life of the people'. Instead of writing such 'querulous' stories, Koz-hevnikov calls upon Solzhenitsyn to 'master the science of joy'.

In the opinion of the editors of this volume, *Matryona's Home* is the finest short story in all post-Stalinist literature.

YURI KAZAKOV (b. 1928) is probably the best young short

story writer in Russia. He was trained as a musician, played the double-bass in jazz and symphony orchestras, and taught at the Moscow Conservatory until he entered the Gorky Literary Institute as a student in 1953. He often travels to the far north, spends most of the year in the village of Tarusa, near his master, the novelist Konstantin Paustovsky. Kazakov flouts every convention of Soviet literature by writing about people who, in one way or another, are alienated from Soviet society: drunkards, vagabonds and, in the case of *Adam and Eve*, an abstract painter. He had been criticized for 'pessimism' and 'decadence' for his fascination with such outcasts.

VASILI AKSYONOV (b. 1932) began his career as a doctor. After four years of practice, he published a weak and rather 'uplifting' novella, *Colleagues*, (1960) which pleased the conservative critics. A second novella, *Starry Ticket* (1961), about a group of Moscow teenagers who leave school in order to have a good time in the Baltic States, was the object of a great controversy. Aksyonov was accused of portraying all Soviet youth as *stilyagi*, teddy boys. *Starry Ticket* and his short stories are immensely popular among young readers who recognize Aksyonov as the first Soviet author to write sensitively and sympathetically about their generation. Aksyonov is also striking for his use of colloquial speech, and the slang of the *stilyagi* in his work.

Leaves and Roots by VOZNESENSKY (*see* Introduction, and note on p. 272) is obviously dedicated to the memory of Boris Pasternak, although the poem first appeared in connexion with the fiftieth anniversary of Leo Tolstoy's death.

Little is known about VICTOR SOSNORA, although, in his idiom and his preoccupations, he is one of the most 'modern' of the young poets. Employed as a factory worker in Leningrad, he has only very recently been accepted for membership in the local Writers' Union—one of the most conservative and provincial of these organizations in the Soviet Union.

Sosnora, who is in his late twenties, has published one volume of poetry (*Yanvarski liven*, Leningrad, 1962).

Although he is of an older generation of poets, BORIS SLUTSKY (b. 1919) published little during the Stalin era. Evtushenko has described a meeting with Slutsky during these years: 'He made a few roubles writing small itms for the radio . . . His desk drawers were stuffed with sad, bitter, grim poems. Slutsky said: "I fought in the war. I'm riddled with bullet holes. And I didn't fight to keep these poems in my desk. But everything will change . . ." ' Since 1953, Slutsky has published a good deal of excellent verse. And although his popularity has never been as great as that of the younger poets, he received a tremendous ovation with his first reading of five anti-Stalin poems in November 1962, at a mass poetry reading.

Good Luck, Schoolboy, which has been excerpted here, is the poet BULAT OKUDZHAVA's first published prose work. It appeared in an anthology, *Tarusa Pages* (1961), sponsored by the novelist Konstantin Paustovsky and published without official sanction. The book was at once withdrawn from circulation, but reappeared on sale after (it is rumoured) Paustovsky appealed to Khrushchev.

Okudzhava (*see* Introduction) was born in Moscow in 1924 of a Georgian father and an Armenian mother. He was wounded at the Front during the Second World War, and later attended Tbilisi University. He then taught school in a small village until 1956 when he came to live in Moscow. He was poetry editor of *Literary Gazette* when that newspaper published Evtushenko's much-attacked poem *Babi Yar*; Okudzhava was later relieved of this job. He is famous in Russia for his poetry readings; tapes of these readings circulate widely, but quite unofficially. He has published two books of verse, and, until he was denounced during the 1962-3 cultural offensive, hoped to publish two major works of fiction.

Yuri Nagibin (b. 1920) has been writing for over twenty years. He was a front-line correspondent during the Second World War, and has published a considerable number of short stories. The quality of his stories has greatly improved in the last few years; today he is one of the best exponents of Soviet 'neo-realism'. Nagibin is not often to be found on the Moscow literary scene; he prefers hunting and fishing in the wilder parts of the Soviet Union. In some of his recent stories like *The Chase*, he shows deep concern and sympathy for the underdog, the victim of circumstances.

Evgeni Evtushenko (*see* Introduction) was born in 1933, in the Siberian village of Zima. Since he published his first poems in 1949, like Mayakovsky, he has alternated between highly personal lyrics, and impassioned 'civic poetry'. Because Evtushenko's best work relies not on imagery but on a remarkably inventive kind of verbal legerdemain (in a uniquely pliable language) his verse is difficult to render in English. In the post-Stalin period, Evtushenko was the first, and by no means the least successful, of the young poets to attempt (in his own words) 'to give back to words their original meaning'.

Until Khrushchev's denunciation of *On Both Sides of the Ocean* (*see* Introduction) in March 1963, Victor Nekrasov (b. 1911) was the most established of the Soviet writers included in this collection. A war hero who returned badly wounded from the Front, Nekrasov won the Stalin prize in 1947 for his splendid novel *In the Trenches of Stalingrad*. Nekrasov's wartime heroism has been equalled by his moral courage in the post-Stalin years. His 1961 novella *Kira Georgievna* has thus far been the only piece of Soviet fiction to suggest the pervasive quality of moral corruption in Stalin's Russia. *On Both Sides of the Ocean*, which has been excerpted here, is the first explicit challenge to the way Soviet writers are expected to describe Western countries. More importantly, however, the views and the hopes expressed by Nekrasov can be said to represent the credo of the best of Russia's new intelligentsia.